NAME _____

## Write the numeral for each number.

three ★ ★ ★ _3_　　　　　　　　one ⭐ ____

five 🪀🪀🪀🪀🪀 ____　　　　　　zero ____

two ▭ ▭ ____　　　　　　　　six ❘❘❘❘❘ ____

eight ● ● ● ● ● ● ● ● ____

ten △ △ △ △ △ △ △ △ △ △ ___

nine ⬡ ⬡ ⬡ ⬡ ⬡ ⬡ ⬡ ⬡ ⬡ ____

seven ♥ ♥ ♥ ♥ ♥ ♥ ♥ ____

four ◼ ◼ ◼ ◼ ____

## Tell how many dots.

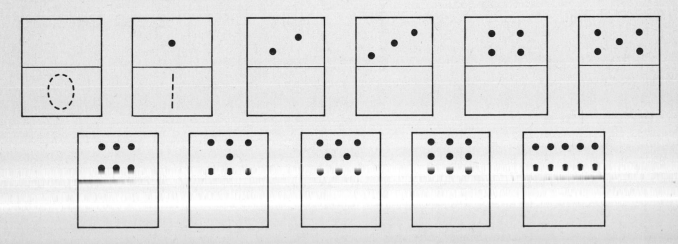

# Facts Through 5

## Add or subtract.

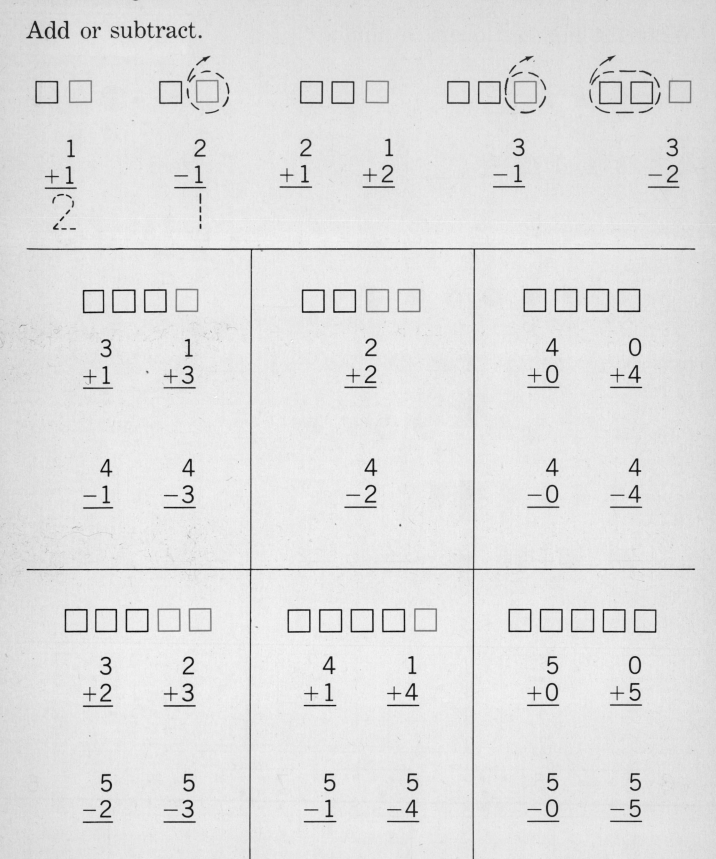

$$\begin{array}{r} 1 \\ +1 \\ \hline 2 \end{array} \qquad \begin{array}{r} 2 \\ -1 \\ \hline \end{array} \qquad \begin{array}{r} 2 \\ +1 \\ \hline \end{array} \qquad \begin{array}{r} 1 \\ +2 \\ \hline \end{array} \qquad \begin{array}{r} 3 \\ -1 \\ \hline \end{array} \qquad \begin{array}{r} 3 \\ -2 \\ \hline \end{array}$$

$$\begin{array}{r} 3 \\ +1 \\ \hline \end{array} \qquad \begin{array}{r} 1 \\ +3 \\ \hline \end{array} \qquad\qquad \begin{array}{r} 2 \\ +2 \\ \hline \end{array} \qquad\qquad \begin{array}{r} 4 \\ +0 \\ \hline \end{array} \qquad \begin{array}{r} 0 \\ +4 \\ \hline \end{array}$$

$$\begin{array}{r} 4 \\ -1 \\ \hline \end{array} \qquad \begin{array}{r} 4 \\ -3 \\ \hline \end{array} \qquad\qquad \begin{array}{r} 4 \\ -2 \\ \hline \end{array} \qquad\qquad \begin{array}{r} 4 \\ -0 \\ \hline \end{array} \qquad \begin{array}{r} 4 \\ -4 \\ \hline \end{array}$$

$$\begin{array}{r} 3 \\ +2 \\ \hline \end{array} \qquad \begin{array}{r} 2 \\ +3 \\ \hline \end{array} \qquad\qquad \begin{array}{r} 4 \\ +1 \\ \hline \end{array} \qquad \begin{array}{r} 1 \\ +4 \\ \hline \end{array} \qquad\qquad \begin{array}{r} 5 \\ +0 \\ \hline \end{array} \qquad \begin{array}{r} 0 \\ +5 \\ \hline \end{array}$$

$$\begin{array}{r} 5 \\ -2 \\ \hline \end{array} \qquad \begin{array}{r} 5 \\ -3 \\ \hline \end{array} \qquad\qquad \begin{array}{r} 5 \\ -1 \\ \hline \end{array} \qquad \begin{array}{r} 5 \\ -4 \\ \hline \end{array} \qquad\qquad \begin{array}{r} 5 \\ -0 \\ \hline \end{array} \qquad \begin{array}{r} 5 \\ -5 \\ \hline \end{array}$$

SPECTRUM MATHEMATICS,
Brown Book-Second Edition

Perfect score: 28    My score: _____

NAME _____

## Add or subtract.

| | | | |
|---|---|---|---|
| 5 | 1 | 6 | 6 |
| +1 | +5 | −1 | −5 |
| 6 | | 5 | |

| | | | | | |
|---|---|---|---|---|---|
| 3 | 6 | 4 | 2 | 6 | 6 |
| +3 | −3 | +2 | +4 | −2 | −4 |

| | | | | | |
|---|---|---|---|---|---|
| 4 | 3 | 5 | 2 | 6 | 1 |
| +3 | +4 | +2 | +5 | +1 | +6 |

| | | | | | |
|---|---|---|---|---|---|
| 7 | 7 | 7 | 7 | 7 | 7 |
| −3 | −4 | −2 | −5 | −1 | −6 |

| | | | | |
|---|---|---|---|---|
| 3 | 5 | 6 | 7 | 7 | 6 |
| +3 | +2 | +0 | −7 | −4 | −2 |

# Facts for 8

## Add or subtract.

|  |  |  |  |
|---|---|---|---|
| $\begin{array}{r} 5 \\ +3 \\ \hline 8 \end{array}$ | $\begin{array}{r} 3 \\ +5 \\ \hline \end{array}$ | $\begin{array}{r} 8 \\ -3 \\ \hline 5 \end{array}$ | $\begin{array}{r} 8 \\ -5 \\ \hline \end{array}$ |

| | | | | | |
|---|---|---|---|---|---|
| $\begin{array}{r} 4 \\ +4 \\ \hline \end{array}$ | | $\begin{array}{r} 6 \\ +2 \\ \hline \end{array}$ | $\begin{array}{r} 2 \\ +6 \\ \hline \end{array}$ | $\begin{array}{r} 7 \\ +1 \\ \hline \end{array}$ | $\begin{array}{r} 1 \\ +7 \\ \hline \end{array}$ |
| $\begin{array}{r} 8 \\ -4 \\ \hline \end{array}$ | | $\begin{array}{r} 8 \\ -2 \\ \hline \end{array}$ | $\begin{array}{r} 8 \\ -6 \\ \hline \end{array}$ | $\begin{array}{r} 8 \\ -1 \\ \hline \end{array}$ | $\begin{array}{r} 8 \\ -7 \\ \hline \end{array}$ |

| | | | | | |
|---|---|---|---|---|---|
| $\begin{array}{r} 2 \\ +6 \\ \hline \end{array}$ | $\begin{array}{r} 4 \\ +3 \\ \hline \end{array}$ | $\begin{array}{r} 5 \\ +1 \\ \hline \end{array}$ | $\begin{array}{r} 3 \\ +5 \\ \hline \end{array}$ | $\begin{array}{r} 7 \\ +1 \\ \hline \end{array}$ | $\begin{array}{r} 0 \\ +8 \\ \hline \end{array}$ |
| $\begin{array}{r} 8 \\ -1 \\ \hline \end{array}$ | $\begin{array}{r} 7 \\ -6 \\ \hline \end{array}$ | $\begin{array}{r} 8 \\ -5 \\ \hline \end{array}$ | $\begin{array}{r} 6 \\ -3 \\ \hline \end{array}$ | $\begin{array}{r} 8 \\ -0 \\ \hline \end{array}$ | $\begin{array}{r} 8 \\ -2 \\ \hline \end{array}$ |

SPECTRUM MATHEMATICS,
Brown Book—Second Edition

Perfect score: 26   My score: _____

NAME _____

# Add or subtract.

| | | | |
|---|---|---|---|
| 5 +4 = 9 | 4 +5 | 9 −4 = 5 | 9 −5 |

| 6 +3 | 3 +6 | 7 +2 | 2 +7 | 8 +1 | 1 +8 |
|---|---|---|---|---|---|
| 9 −3 | 9 −6 | 9 −2 | 9 −7 | 9 −1 | 9 −8 |

| 5 +4 | 2 +7 | 6 +1 | 9 +0 | 1 +8 | 4 +4 |
|---|---|---|---|---|---|

| 9 −5 | 7 −3 | 9 −8 | 9 −3 | 9 −9 | 9 −0 |
|---|---|---|---|---|---|

# Facts for 10

## Add or subtract.

5
+5
10

10
−5
5

6          4
+4        +6

10        10
−4        −6

7          3
+3        +7

10        10
−3        −7

8          2
+2        +8

10        10
−2        −8

9          1
+1        +9

10        10
−1        −9

4          5          9
+6        +5        +1

10        10        10
−8        −3        −0

SPECTRUM MATHEMATICS,
Brown Book–Second Edition

Perfect score: 24     My score: _____

## Addition Facts Through 10

### Add.

| | | | | | |
|---|---|---|---|---|---|
| 1 <br> +4 <br> **5** | 0 <br> +7 | 3 <br> +6 | 6 <br> +4 | 2 <br> +1 | 0 <br> +0 |
| 1 <br> +1 | 3 <br> +2 | 7 <br> +2 | 7 <br> +3 | 4 <br> +2 | 3 <br> +5 |
| 0 <br> +5 | 3 <br> +1 | 3 <br> +3 | 2 <br> +6 | 7 <br> +1 | 6 <br> +3 |
| 5 <br> +4 | 4 <br> +3 | 1 <br> +2 | 5 <br> +3 | 4 <br> +6 | 4 <br> +4 |
| 0 <br> +6 | 4 <br> +1 | 8 <br> +1 | 9 <br> +1 | 8 <br> +2 | 2 <br> +2 |
| 2 <br> +7 | 5 <br> +2 | 1 <br> +6 | 5 <br> +5 | 4 <br> +5 | 6 <br> +2 |

SPECTRUM MATHEMATICS,
Brown Book–Second Edition

Perfect score: 36     My score: _____

# Subtraction Facts Through 10

## Subtract.

| | | | | | |
|---|---|---|---|---|---|
| 8<br>−1<br>7 | 6<br>−3 | 5<br>−2 | 3<br>−1 | 9<br>−5 | 4<br>−4 |
| 7<br>−3 | 5<br>−4 | 4<br>−2 | 8<br>−3 | 9<br>−9 | 0<br>−0 |
| 10<br>−3 | 9<br>−7 | 7<br>−5 | 8<br>−4 | 6<br>−1 | 8<br>−7 |
| 10<br>−6 | 8<br>−2 | 5<br>−3 | 7<br>−6 | 4<br>−3 | 10<br>−5 |
| 9<br>−3 | 10<br>−2 | 7<br>−2 | 8<br>−6 | 10<br>−9 | 8<br>−8 |
| 10<br>−4 | 9<br>−6 | 9<br>−8 | 8<br>−1 | 10<br>−7 | 7<br>−4 |

SPECTRUM MATHEMATICS,
Brown Book–Second Edition

Perfect score: 36    My score: _____

Solve each problem.

$$\begin{array}{r} 4 \\ + 3 \\ \hline 7 \end{array}$$

leaves on the ground

leaves falling

leaves in all

---

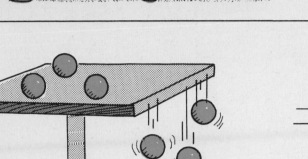

_____ balls in all

− _____ balls falling

_____ balls not falling

---

_____ fish by a rock

+ _____ more fish coming

_____ fish in all

---

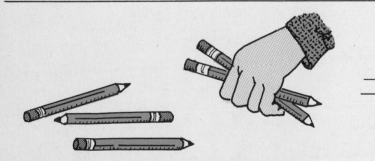

_____ pencils in all

− _____ pencils taken

_____ pencils not taken

---

_____ puppies on a rug

+ _____ more puppies coming

_____ puppies in all

**Checkup**

## Add.

| | | | | | |
|---|---|---|---|---|---|
| 2 | 7 | 4 | 6 | 2 | 0 |
| +4 | +3 | +5 | +2 | +3 | +4 |

| | | | | | |
|---|---|---|---|---|---|
| 4 | 1 | 2 | 3 | 6 | 2 |
| +3 | +5 | +8 | +3 | +4 | +1 |

| | | | | | |
|---|---|---|---|---|---|
| 3 | 7 | 8 | 5 | 3 | 5 |
| +1 | +0 | +1 | +2 | +6 | +5 |

## Subtract.

| | | | | | |
|---|---|---|---|---|---|
| 3 | 5 | 10 | 9 | 7 | 10 |
| −3 | −2 | − 6 | −2 | −3 | − 5 |

| | | | | | |
|---|---|---|---|---|---|
| 9 | 8 | 1 | 6 | 8 | 10 |
| −1 | −7 | −0 | −4 | −5 | − 8 |

| | | | | | |
|---|---|---|---|---|---|
| 9 | 4 | 6 | 7 | 10 | 8 |
| −6 | −3 | −3 | −5 | − 9 | −4 |

SPECTRUM MATHEMATICS,
Brown Book–Second Edition

Perfect score: 36    My score: _____

NAME _____

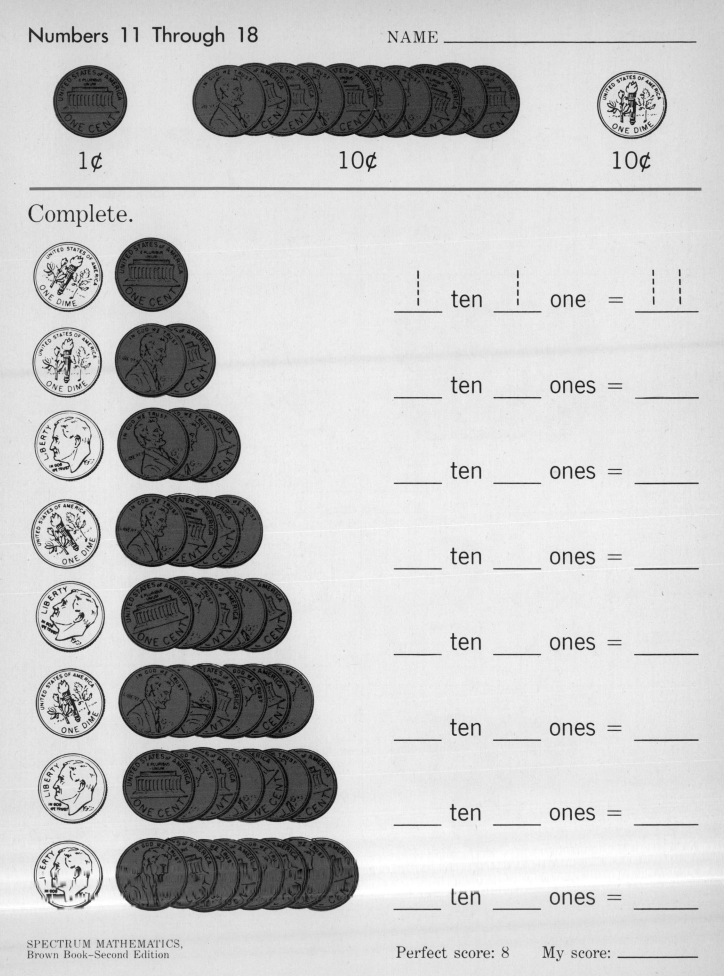

1¢          10¢          10¢

## Complete.

___ ten ___ one  =  ___

___ ten ___ ones  =  ___

___ ten ___ ones  =  ___

___ ten ___ ones  =  ___

___ ten ___ ones  =  ___

___ ten ___ ones  =  ___

___ ten ___ ones  =  ___

___ ten ___ ones  =  ___

SPECTRUM MATHEMATICS,
Brown Book–Second Edition

Perfect score: 8     My score: _____

Complete.

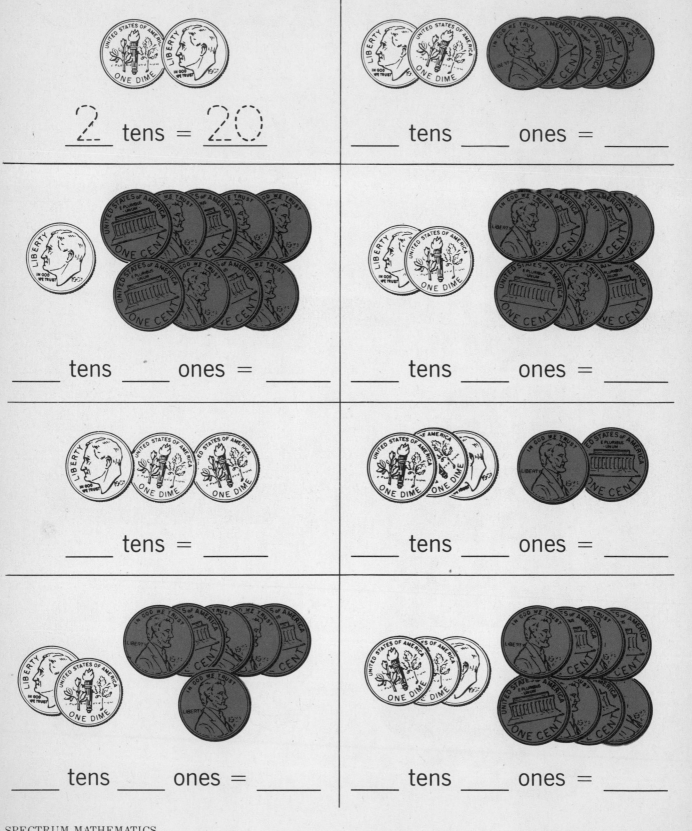

_2_ tens = 20

_____ tens _____ ones = _____

_____ tens _____ ones = _____

_____ tens _____ ones = _____

_____ tens = _____

_____ tens _____ ones = _____

_____ tens _____ ones = _____

_____ tens _____ ones = _____

SPECTRUM MATHEMATICS,
Brown Book—Second Edition

Perfect score: 8    My score: _____

# Numbers 40 Through 99

NAME _____

## Complete.

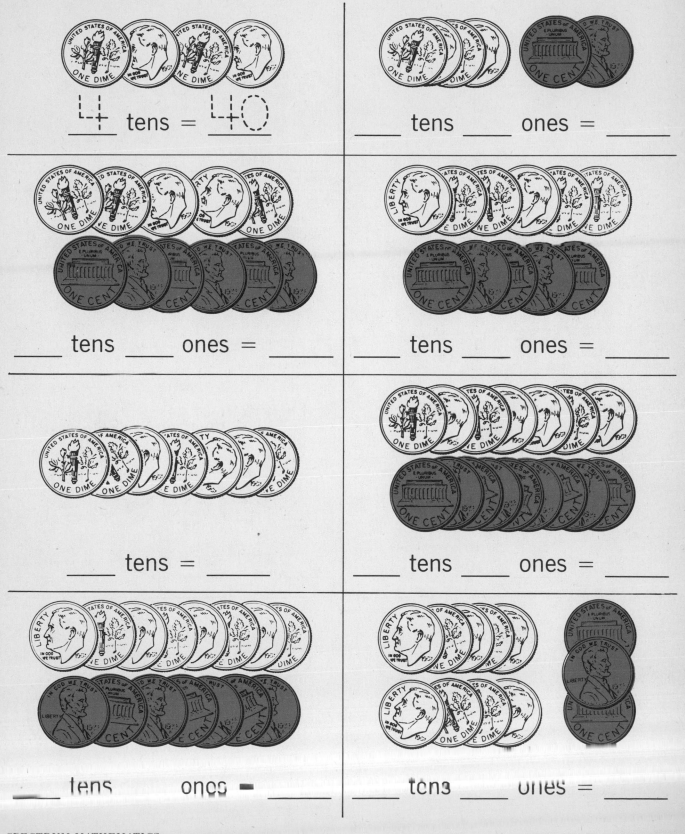

___4___ tens = __40__

___ tens ___ ones = _____

___ tens ___ ones = _____

___ tens ___ ones = _____

___ tens = _____

___ tens ___ ones = _____

___ tens ___ ones = _____

___ tens ___ ones = _____

# Numbers 40 Through 99

## Complete.

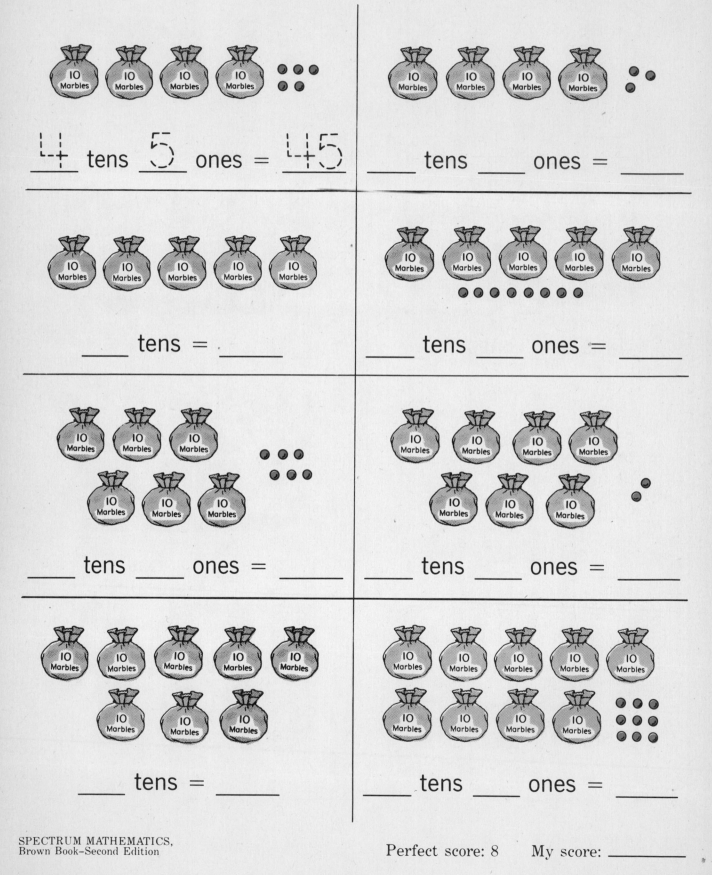

__4__ tens __5__ ones = __45__

____ tens ____ ones = _____

____ tens = _____

____ tens ____ ones = _____

____ tens ____ ones = _____

____ tens ____ ones = _____

____ tens = _____

____ tens ____ ones = _____

SPECTRUM MATHEMATICS,
Brown Book–Second Edition

Perfect score: 8    My score: _____

14

NAME _____

Complete.

4 tens 6 ones = $46$          2 tens 1 one  = _____

1 ten  2 ones = _____          5 tens 7 ones = _____

3 tens 7 ones = _____          1 ten  9 ones = _____

2 tens 4 ones = _____          8 tens 8 ones = _____

9 tens = _____                 6 tens 7 ones = _____

6 tens = _____                 7 tens 2 ones = _____

5 tens 3 ones = _____          9 tens 5 ones = _____

7 tens 8 ones = _____          4 tens 1 one  = _____

1 ten 1 one  = _____           3 tens 4 ones = _____

8 tens 4 ones = _____          6 tens 6 ones = _____

3 tens 5 ones = _____          8 tens 9 ones = _____

4 tens 9 ones = _____          2 tens =

9 tens 6 ones = _____          5 tens = _____

# Name numbers in order.

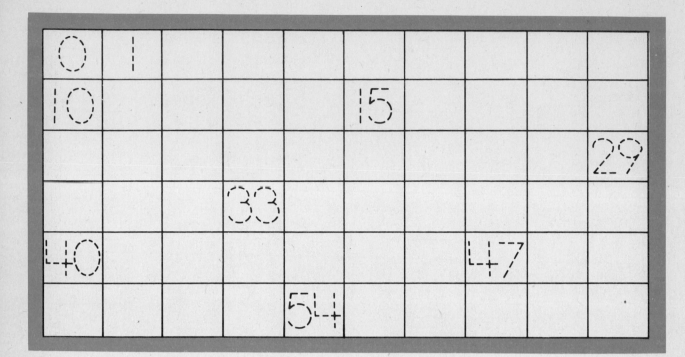

## Connect the dots in order.

Start here.

96•
95•
93•
92•

97  60
    61
94  64
65

•62
•63

70 71
69•
  •72

91
90  83
88 89
87  84  82
86  85

81  74
80• •75
79•   •76
  78  •77

•67
68•

•73

NAME _____

Name the next four numbers.

6, 7, 8, _9_, _10_, _11_, _12_

22, 23, 24, _____, _____, _____, _____

37, 38, 39, _____, _____, _____, _____

15, 16, 17, _____, _____, _____, _____

51, 52, 53, _____, _____, _____, _____

44, 45, 46, _____, _____, _____, _____

76, 77, 78, _____, _____, _____, _____

82, 83, 84, _____, _____, _____, _____

68, 69, 70, _____, _____, _____, _____

86, 87, 88, _____, _____, _____, _____

55, 56, 57, _____, _____, _____, _____

93, 94, 95, _____, _____, _____, _____

# Addition Facts Through 10

## Add.
## If you get 9, color that part.

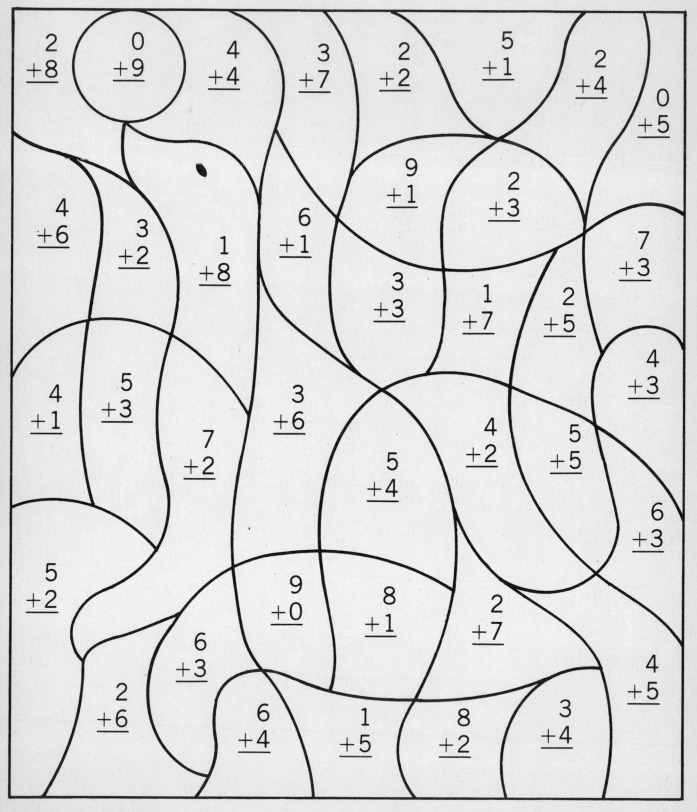

$$\begin{array}{cc} 2 \\ +8 \end{array} \quad \begin{array}{cc} 0 \\ +9 \end{array} \quad \begin{array}{cc} 4 \\ +4 \end{array} \quad \begin{array}{cc} 3 \\ +7 \end{array} \quad \begin{array}{cc} 2 \\ +2 \end{array} \quad \begin{array}{cc} 5 \\ +1 \end{array} \quad \begin{array}{cc} 2 \\ +4 \end{array} \quad \begin{array}{cc} 0 \\ +5 \end{array}$$

$$\begin{array}{cc} 9 \\ +1 \end{array} \qquad \begin{array}{cc} 2 \\ +3 \end{array}$$

$$\begin{array}{cc} 4 \\ +6 \end{array} \quad \begin{array}{cc} 3 \\ +2 \end{array} \quad \begin{array}{cc} 1 \\ +8 \end{array} \quad \begin{array}{cc} 6 \\ +1 \end{array} \qquad \qquad \begin{array}{cc} 7 \\ +3 \end{array}$$

$$\begin{array}{cc} 3 \\ +3 \end{array} \quad \begin{array}{cc} 1 \\ +7 \end{array} \quad \begin{array}{cc} 2 \\ +5 \end{array}$$

$$\begin{array}{cc} 4 \\ +3 \end{array}$$

$$\begin{array}{cc} 4 \\ +1 \end{array} \quad \begin{array}{cc} 5 \\ +3 \end{array} \quad \begin{array}{cc} 3 \\ +6 \end{array}$$

$$\begin{array}{cc} 7 \\ +2 \end{array} \qquad \begin{array}{cc} 4 \\ +2 \end{array} \quad \begin{array}{cc} 5 \\ +5 \end{array}$$

$$\begin{array}{cc} 5 \\ +4 \end{array} \qquad \qquad \begin{array}{cc} 6 \\ +3 \end{array}$$

$$\begin{array}{cc} 5 \\ +2 \end{array} \qquad \begin{array}{cc} 9 \\ +0 \end{array} \quad \begin{array}{cc} 8 \\ +1 \end{array} \quad \begin{array}{cc} 2 \\ +7 \end{array}$$

$$\begin{array}{cc} 6 \\ +3 \end{array} \qquad \qquad \qquad \begin{array}{cc} 4 \\ +5 \end{array}$$

$$\begin{array}{cc} 2 \\ +6 \end{array} \quad \begin{array}{cc} 6 \\ +4 \end{array} \quad \begin{array}{cc} 1 \\ +5 \end{array} \quad \begin{array}{cc} 8 \\ +2 \end{array} \quad \begin{array}{cc} 3 \\ +4 \end{array}$$

NAME _____

## How is a puppy like a penny?

| 0 | 1 | 2 | 3 | 4 | 5 | 6 | 7 | 8 | 9 |
|---|---|---|---|---|---|---|---|---|---|
| T | N | S | A | D | H | I | L | E | C |

Subtract. Write the letter for each answer.

$$\begin{array}{r} 9 \\ -1 \\ \hline \end{array} \quad \begin{array}{r} 5 \\ -2 \\ \hline \end{array} \quad \begin{array}{r} 9 \\ -0 \\ \hline \end{array} \quad \begin{array}{r} 7 \\ -2 \\ \hline \end{array} \qquad \begin{array}{r} 9 \\ -4 \\ \hline \end{array} \quad \begin{array}{r} 8 \\ -5 \\ \hline \end{array} \quad \begin{array}{r} 8 \\ -6 \\ \hline \end{array} \qquad \begin{array}{r} 3 \\ -0 \\ \hline \end{array}$$

E

$$\begin{array}{r} 8 \\ -3 \\ \hline \end{array} \quad \begin{array}{r} 8 \\ -0 \\ \hline \end{array} \quad \begin{array}{r} 7 \\ -4 \\ \hline \end{array} \quad \begin{array}{r} 9 \\ -5 \\ \hline \end{array} \qquad \begin{array}{r} 4 \\ -1 \\ \hline \end{array} \quad \begin{array}{r} 10 \\ -9 \\ \hline \end{array} \quad \begin{array}{r} 7 \\ -3 \\ \hline \end{array}$$

$$\begin{array}{r} 10 \\ -7 \\ \hline \end{array} \qquad \begin{array}{r} 8 \\ -8 \\ \hline \end{array} \quad \begin{array}{r} 9 \\ -6 \\ \hline \end{array} \quad \begin{array}{r} 10 \\ -4 \\ \hline \end{array} \quad \begin{array}{r} 7 \\ -0 \\ \hline \end{array}$$

**Checkup**

Complete.

2 tens 8 ones = _____     |     5 tens = _____

3 tens 1 one  = _____     |     4 tens 5 ones = _____

7 tens = _____            |     8 tens 2 ones = _____

6 tens 6 ones = _____     |     9 tens 8 ones = _____

9 tens = _____            |     7 tens 9 ones = _____

Name the next four numbers.

4, 5, 6, _____, _____, _____, _____

37, 38, 39, _____, _____, _____, _____

53, 54, 55, _____, _____, _____, _____

61, 62, 63, _____, _____, _____, _____

78, 79, 80, _____, _____, _____, _____

86, 87, 88, _____, _____, _____, _____

**Centimeter**

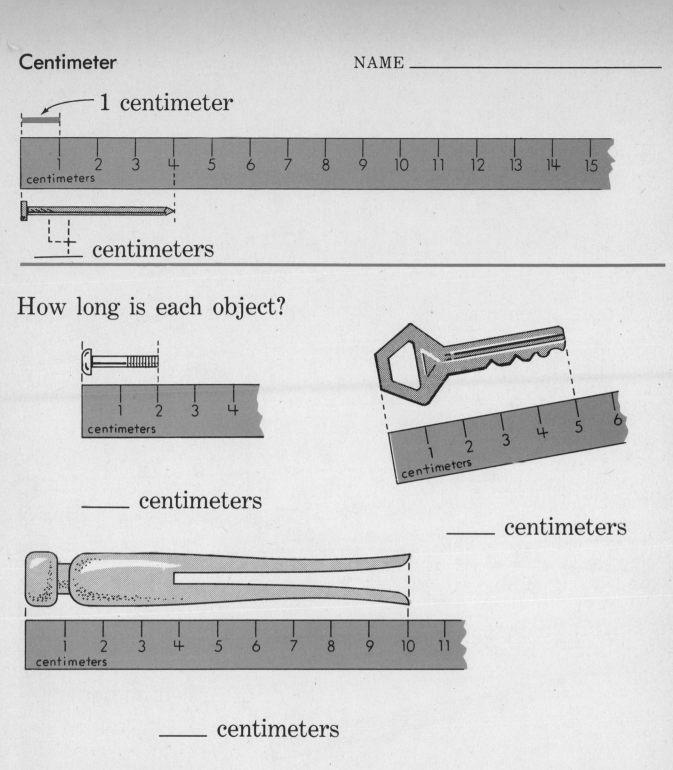

1 centimeter

| | | | | | | | | | | | | | | |
centimeters 1 2 3 4 5 6 7 8 9 10 11 12 13 14 15

_____ centimeters

How long is each object?

_____ centimeters

centimeters 1 2 3 4

_____ centimeters

_____ centimeters

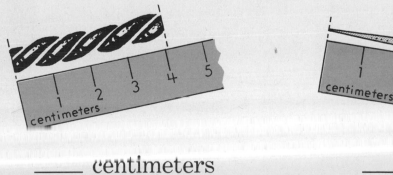

_____ centimeters

_____ centimeters

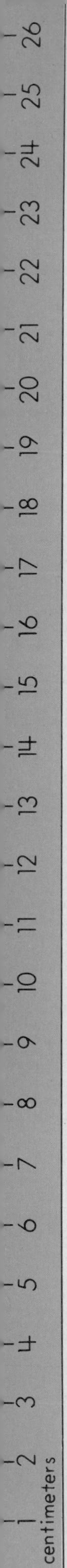

**Centimeter**

← Cut off this ruler.

How long is each object?

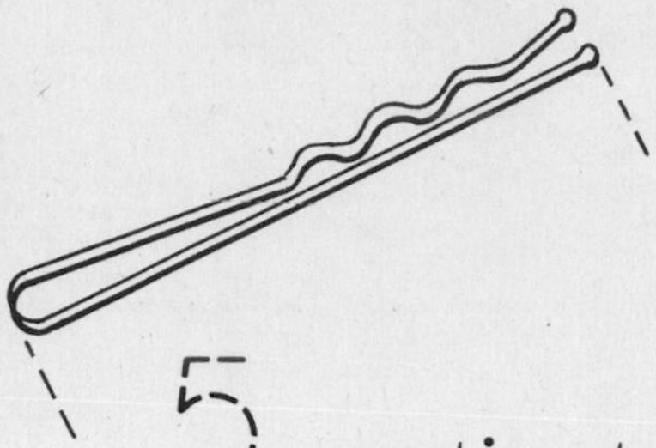

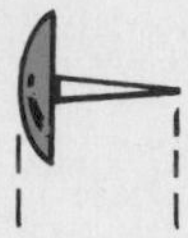

5 centimeters

____ centimeter

____ centimeters

____ centimeters

____ centimeters

____ centimeters

____ centimeters

____ centimeters



Perfect score: 8 My score: ________

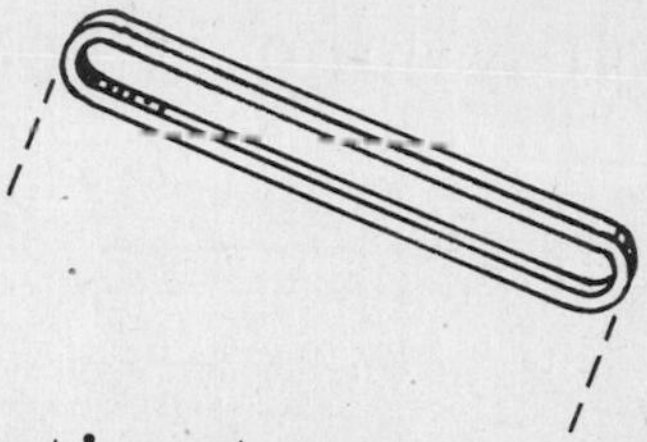

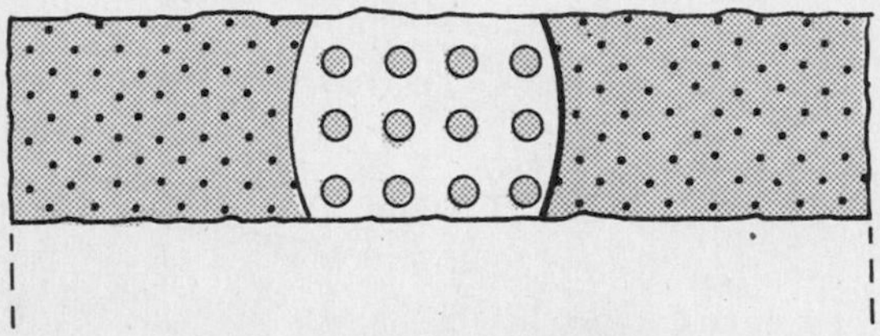

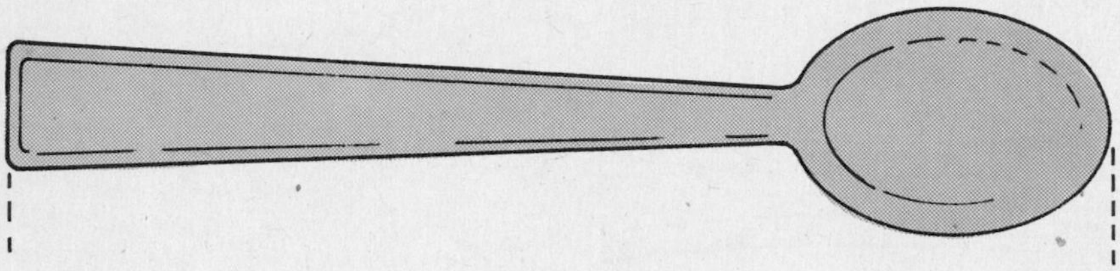

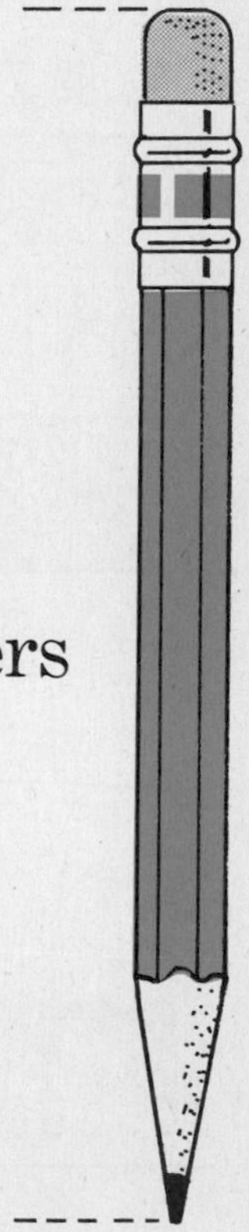

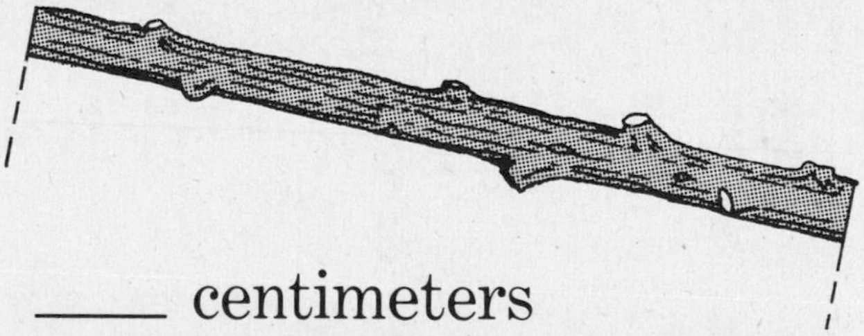

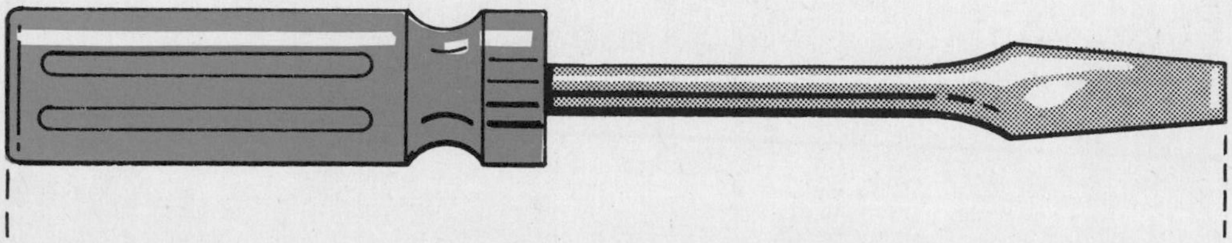

# Inch

NAME _____

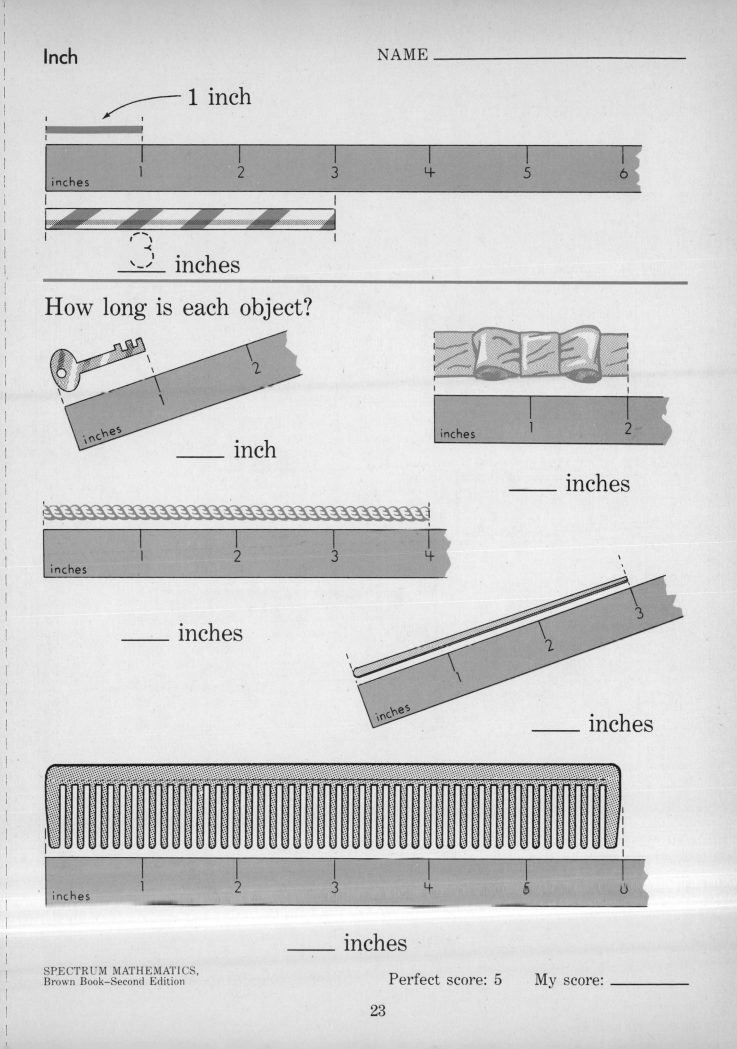

1 inch

inches  1  2  3  4  5  6

___ inches

## How long is each object?

inches

___ inch

inches  1  2

___ inches

inches  1  2  3  4

___ inches

inches  1  2  3

___ inches

inches  1  2  3  4  5  6

___ inches

SPECTRUM MATHEMATICS,
Brown Book–Second Edition

Perfect score: 5    My score: _____

23

# Inch

←Cut off this ruler.

How long is each object?

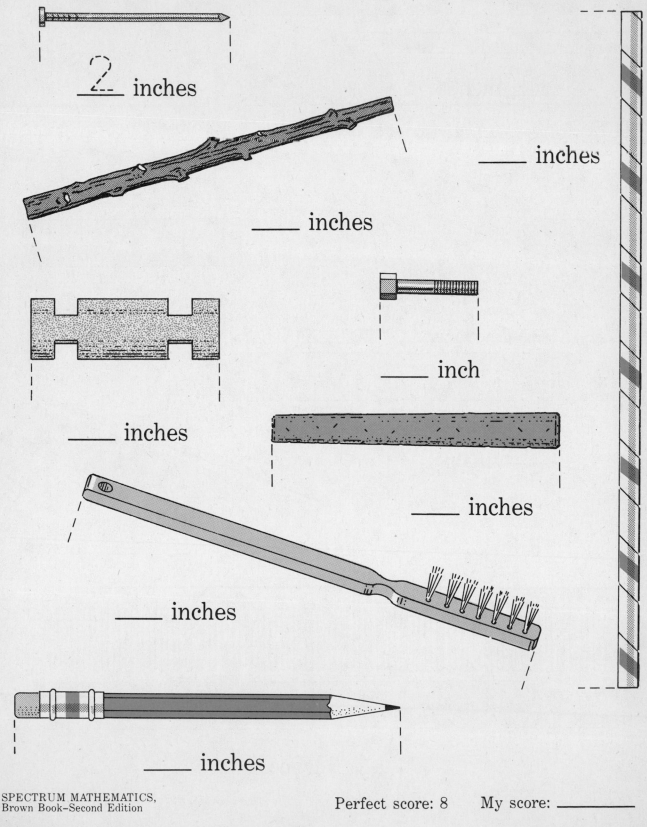

_2_ inches

_____ inches

_____ inches

_____ inches

_____ inch

_____ inches

_____ inches

_____ inches

SPECTRUM MATHEMATICS,
Brown Book–Second Edition

Perfect score: 8    My score: _____

**Checkup**

Use a centimeter ruler.

How long is each object?

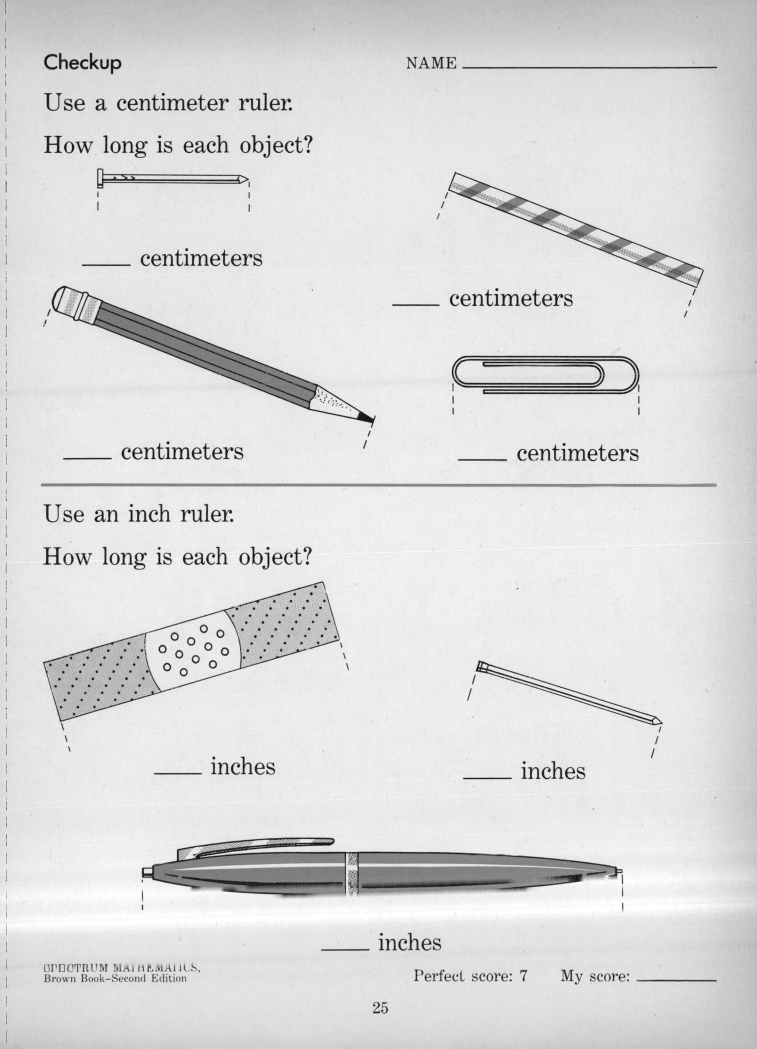

_____ centimeters

_____ centimeters

_____ centimeters

_____ centimeters

Use an inch ruler.

How long is each object?

_____ inches

_____ inches

_____ inches

SPECTRUM MATHEMATICS,
Brown Book–Second Edition

Perfect score: 7    My score: _____

# Facts for 11

## Add or subtract.

| | | | | | |
|---|---|---|---|---|---|
| 8<br>+3<br>¦¦ | | 3<br>+8 | 1 1<br>− 8<br>(3) | | 1 1<br>− 3 |
| 9<br>+2 | | 2<br>+9 | 1 1<br>− 9 | | 1 1<br>− 2 |
| 6<br>+5 | | 5<br>+6 | 1 1<br>− 6 | | 1 1<br>− 5 |
| 7<br>+4 | | 4<br>+7 | 1 1<br>− 7 | | 1 1<br>− 4 |

| | | | | | |
|---|---|---|---|---|---|
| 7<br>+4 | 6<br>+5 | 3<br>+8 | 1 1<br>− 6 | 1 1<br>− 9 | 1 1<br>− 7 |
| 1 1<br>+ 0 | 9<br>+2 | 5<br>+6 | 1 1<br>− 2 | 1 1<br>− 0 | 1 1<br>− 8 |

SPECTRUM MATHEMATICS,
Brown Book–Second Edition

Perfect score: 28    My score: _____

26

# Facts for 12

## Add or subtract.

$$\begin{array}{r} 8 \\ +4 \\ \hline 12 \end{array} \qquad \begin{array}{r} 4 \\ +8 \\ \hline \end{array} \qquad \begin{array}{r} 12 \\ -8 \\ \hline 4 \end{array} \qquad \begin{array}{r} 12 \\ -4 \\ \hline \end{array}$$

$$\begin{array}{r} 9 \\ +3 \\ \hline \end{array} \qquad \begin{array}{r} 3 \\ +9 \\ \hline \end{array} \qquad \begin{array}{r} 12 \\ -9 \\ \hline \end{array} \qquad \begin{array}{r} 12 \\ -3 \\ \hline \end{array}$$

$$\begin{array}{r} 7 \\ +5 \\ \hline \end{array} \qquad \begin{array}{r} 5 \\ +7 \\ \hline \end{array} \qquad \begin{array}{r} 12 \\ -7 \\ \hline \end{array} \qquad \begin{array}{r} 12 \\ -5 \\ \hline \end{array}$$

$$\begin{array}{r} 6 \\ +6 \\ \hline \end{array} \qquad \qquad \begin{array}{r} 12 \\ -6 \\ \hline \end{array}$$

$$\begin{array}{r} 9 \\ +3 \\ \hline \end{array} \qquad \begin{array}{r} 5 \\ +7 \\ \hline \end{array} \qquad \begin{array}{r} 12 \\ +0 \\ \hline \end{array} \qquad \begin{array}{r} 12 \\ -6 \\ \hline \end{array} \qquad \begin{array}{r} 12 \\ -0 \\ \hline \end{array} \qquad \begin{array}{r} 12 \\ -8 \\ \hline \end{array}$$

$$\begin{array}{r} 6 \\ +6 \\ \hline \end{array} \qquad \begin{array}{r} 4 \\ +8 \\ \hline \end{array} \qquad \begin{array}{r} 7 \\ +5 \\ \hline \end{array} \qquad \begin{array}{r} 12 \\ -5 \\ \hline \end{array} \qquad \begin{array}{r} 12 \\ -9 \\ \hline \end{array} \qquad \begin{array}{r} 12 \\ -4 \\ \hline \end{array}$$

SPECTRUM MATHEMATICS,
Brown Book–Second Edition

Perfect score: 26    My score: _____

## Add.

| | | | | | |
|---|---|---|---|---|---|
| 8<br>+4<br>12 | 7<br>+4 | 6<br>+6 | 3<br>+9 | 9<br>+2 | 6<br>+5 |
| 5<br>+5 | 7<br>+5 | 9<br>+1 | 4<br>+8 | 5<br>+7 | 3<br>+8 |
| 4<br>+6 | 2<br>+9 | 8<br>+3 | 4<br>+7 | 9<br>+3 | 5<br>+6 |

## Subtract.

| | | | | | |
|---|---|---|---|---|---|
| 12<br>− 8<br>4 | 11<br>− 9 | 12<br>− 5 | 11<br>− 4 | 12<br>− 6 | 11<br>− 0 |
| 12<br>− 3 | 12<br>− 7 | 10<br>− 3 | 11<br>− 8 | 10<br>− 6 | 11<br>− 5 |
| 12<br>− 0 | 11<br>− 2 | 10<br>− 8 | 12<br>− 4 | 11<br>− 7 | 12<br>− 9 |

SPECTRUM MATHEMATICS,
Brown Book–Second Edition

Perfect score: 36    My score: _____

Solve each problem.

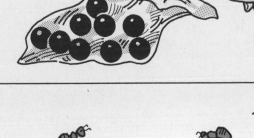 

$$
\begin{array}{r}
8 \\
+\ 3 \\
\hline
11
\end{array}
$$

crayons in a box

more crayons

crayons in all

---

$$
\begin{array}{r}
\phantom{0} \\
+\ \underline{\phantom{00}} \\
\end{array}
$$

birds on a wire

birds coming

birds in all

---

$$
\begin{array}{r}
\phantom{0} \\
+\ \underline{\phantom{00}} \\
\end{array}
$$

orange hats

black hats

hats in all

---

$$
\begin{array}{r}
\phantom{0} \\
+\ \underline{\phantom{00}} \\
\end{array}
$$

marbles in a bag

marbles are put in

marbles in all

---

$$
\begin{array}{r}
\phantom{0} \\
+\ \underline{\phantom{00}} \\
\end{array}
$$

ants on a hill

ants coming

ants in all

SPECTRUM MATHEMATICS,
Brown Book–Second Edition

Perfect score: 5     My score: _____

# Problems

Solve each problem.

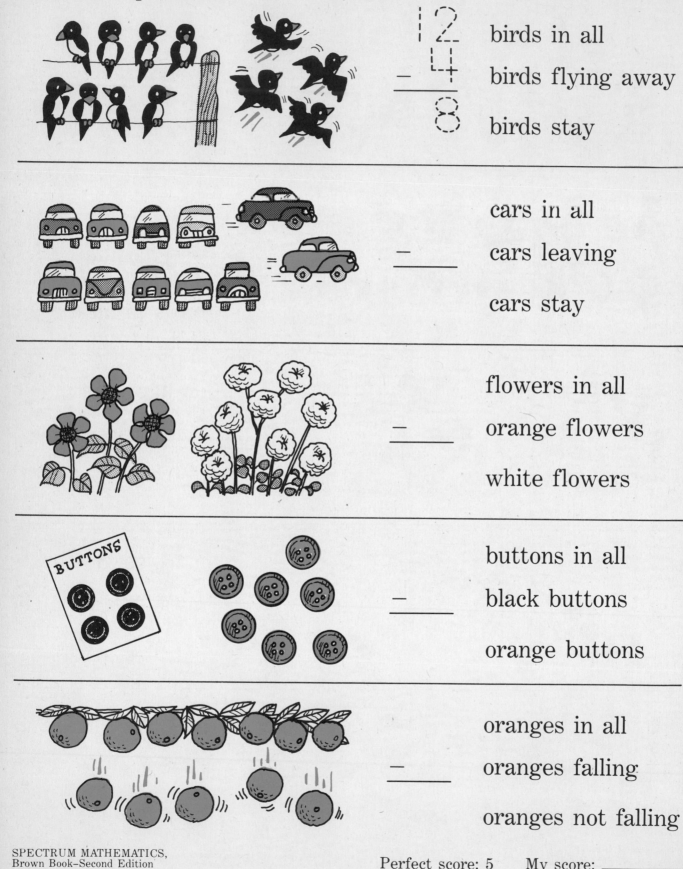

12
− 4
8    birds in all
     birds flying away
     birds stay

___
     cars in all
−    cars leaving
     cars stay

___
     flowers in all
−    orange flowers
     white flowers

___
     buttons in all
−    black buttons
     orange buttons

___
     oranges in all
−    oranges falling
     oranges not falling

SPECTRUM MATHEMATICS,
Brown Book–Second Edition

Perfect score: 5    My score: _____

# Add or subtract.

| | | | | | |
|---|---|---|---|---|---|
| 7 +6 = 13 | | 6 +7 | 13 −7 = 6 | | 13 −6 |
| 8 +5 | | 5 +8 | 13 −8 | | 13 −5 |
| 9 +4 | | 4 +9 | 13 −9 | | 13 −4 |

| 5 +8 | 9 +4 | 7 +6 | 13 −5 | 13 −7 | 13 −9 |
|---|---|---|---|---|---|

| 6 +7 | 8 +5 | 4 +9 | 13 −4 | 13 −8 | 13 −6 |
|---|---|---|---|---|---|

# Facts for 14

## Add or subtract.

$$
\begin{array}{r} 9 \\ +5 \\ \hline 14 \end{array}
\qquad
\begin{array}{r} 5 \\ +9 \\ \hline \end{array}
\qquad
\begin{array}{r} 14 \\ -9 \\ \hline 5 \end{array}
\qquad
\begin{array}{r} 14 \\ -5 \\ \hline \end{array}
$$

$$
\begin{array}{r} 8 \\ +6 \\ \hline \end{array}
\qquad
\begin{array}{r} 6 \\ +8 \\ \hline \end{array}
\qquad
\begin{array}{r} 14 \\ -8 \\ \hline \end{array}
\qquad
\begin{array}{r} 14 \\ -6 \\ \hline \end{array}
$$

$$
\begin{array}{r} 7 \\ +7 \\ \hline \end{array}
\qquad
\begin{array}{r} 14 \\ -7 \\ \hline \end{array}
$$

$$
\begin{array}{r} 8 \\ +6 \\ \hline \end{array}
\qquad
\begin{array}{r} 7 \\ +7 \\ \hline \end{array}
\qquad
\begin{array}{r} 6 \\ +6 \\ \hline \end{array}
\qquad
\begin{array}{r} 14 \\ -8 \\ \hline \end{array}
\qquad
\begin{array}{r} 12 \\ -7 \\ \hline \end{array}
\qquad
\begin{array}{r} 14 \\ -5 \\ \hline \end{array}
$$

$$
\begin{array}{r} 9 \\ +4 \\ \hline \end{array}
\qquad
\begin{array}{r} 5 \\ +9 \\ \hline \end{array}
\qquad
\begin{array}{r} 7 \\ +4 \\ \hline \end{array}
\qquad
\begin{array}{r} 14 \\ -7 \\ \hline \end{array}
\qquad
\begin{array}{r} 13 \\ -8 \\ \hline \end{array}
\qquad
\begin{array}{r} 14 \\ -6 \\ \hline \end{array}
$$

$$
\begin{array}{r} 9 \\ +5 \\ \hline \end{array}
\qquad
\begin{array}{r} 6 \\ +7 \\ \hline \end{array}
\qquad
\begin{array}{r} 6 \\ +8 \\ \hline \end{array}
\qquad
\begin{array}{r} 11 \\ -8 \\ \hline \end{array}
\qquad
\begin{array}{r} 14 \\ -9 \\ \hline \end{array}
\qquad
\begin{array}{r} 12 \\ -4 \\ \hline \end{array}
$$

SPECTRUM MATHEMATICS,
Brown Book–Second Edition

Perfect score: 28    My score: _____

NAME _____

## Add.

| | | | | | |
|---|---|---|---|---|---|
| 9<br>+4 | 7<br>+7 | 6<br>+5 | 8<br>+4 | 5<br>+9 | 4<br>+7 |
| 13 | | | | | |

| | | | | | |
|---|---|---|---|---|---|
| 5<br>+6 | 9<br>+5 | 5<br>+7 | 8<br>+5 | 7<br>+6 | 6<br>+8 |

| | | | | | |
|---|---|---|---|---|---|
| 3<br>+8 | 7<br>+5 | 8<br>+6 | 5<br>+8 | 4<br>+9 | 6<br>+6 |

## Subtract.

| | | | | | |
|---|---|---|---|---|---|
| 12<br>− 5 | 13<br>− 7 | 14<br>− 5 | 11<br>− 3 | 14<br>− 7 | 13<br>− 6 |
| 7 | | | | | |

| | | | | | |
|---|---|---|---|---|---|
| 13<br>− 8 | 12<br>− 9 | 14<br>− 6 | 11<br>− 5 | 14<br>− 9 | 12<br>− 6 |

| | | | | | |
|---|---|---|---|---|---|
| 11<br>− 7 | 11<br>− 9 | 13<br>− 4 | 12<br>− 8 | 13<br>− 9 | 14<br>− 8 |

# Problems

Solve each problem.

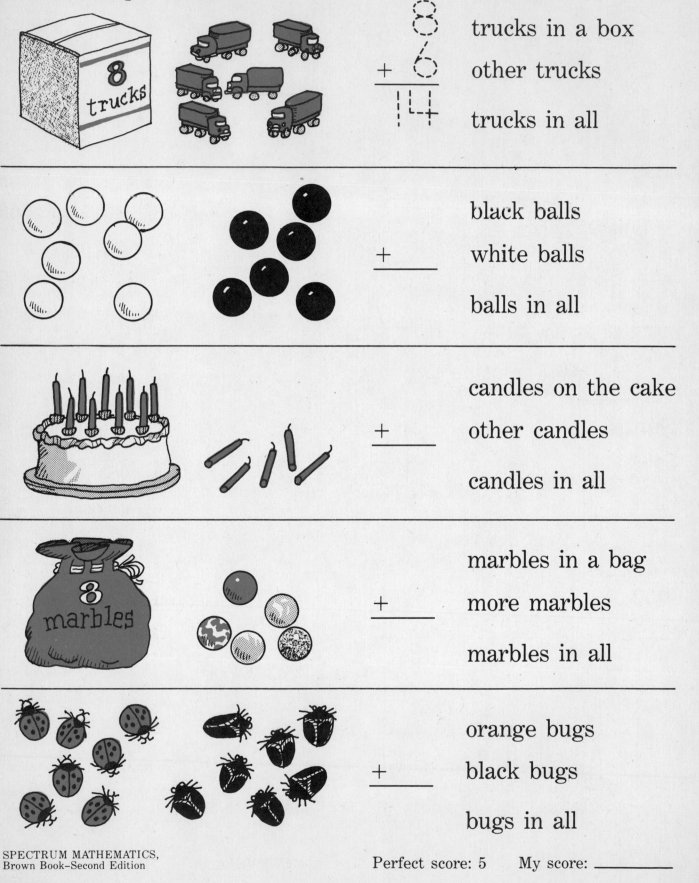

$8$ trucks in a box

$+ 6$ other trucks

$14$ trucks in all

_____ black balls

$+$ _____ white balls

_____ balls in all

_____ candles on the cake

$+$ _____ other candles

_____ candles in all

_____ marbles in a bag

$+$ _____ more marbles

_____ marbles in all

_____ orange bugs

$+$ _____ black bugs

_____ bugs in all

SPECTRUM MATHEMATICS,
Brown Book–Second Edition

Perfect score: 5    My score: _____

**Problems**

Solve each problem.

13  turtles in all
– 4  turtles going away
_____
9  turtles stay

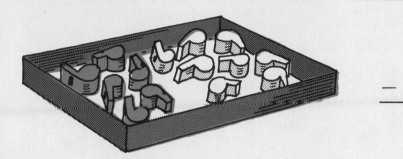

_____  whistles in the box
–      white whistles
_____
       orange whistles

_____  leaves in all
–      leaves falling
_____
       leaves not falling

_____  eggs in all
–      eggs broken
_____
       eggs not broken

_____  candles in all
–      candles lit
_____
       candles not lit

SPECTRUM MATHEMATICS,
Brown Book—Second Edition

Perfect score: 5    My score: _____

Add or subtract.

```
* * * *   * * * *
* * * *   * * *
```

```
   8          7         1 5        1 5
  +7         +8         - 7        - 8
  ‾‾‾        ‾‾‾        ‾‾‾        ‾‾‾
  15                     8
```

```
* * * * *   * * *
* * * *     * * *
```

```
   9          6         1 5        1 5
  +6         +9         - 6        - 9
  ‾‾‾        ‾‾‾        ‾‾‾        ‾‾‾
```

```
   6      7      8  │  1 4     1 5     1 3
  +9     +8     +6  │  - 9     - 8     - 7
  ‾‾     ‾‾     ‾‾  │  ‾‾‾     ‾‾‾     ‾‾‾

   6      9      8  │  1 5     1 4     1 5
  +8     +5     +7  │  - 9     - 6     - 7
  ‾‾     ‾‾     ‾‾  │  ‾‾‾     ‾‾‾     ‾‾‾

   8      9      7  │  1 3     1 5     1 4
  +5     +6     +7  │  - 8     - 6     - 5
  ‾‾     ‾‾     ‾‾  │  ‾‾‾     ‾‾‾     ‾‾‾
```

# Facts for 16

## Add or subtract.

$$\begin{array}{r} 9 \\ +7 \\ \hline 16 \end{array} \qquad \begin{array}{r} 7 \\ +9 \\ \hline \end{array} \qquad \begin{array}{r} 1\,6 \\ -7 \\ \hline 9 \end{array} \qquad \begin{array}{r} 1\,6 \\ -9 \\ \hline \end{array}$$

$$\begin{array}{r} 8 \\ +8 \\ \hline \end{array} \qquad\qquad\qquad \begin{array}{r} 1\,6 \\ -8 \\ \hline \end{array}$$

$$\begin{array}{r} 8 \\ +7 \\ \hline \end{array} \qquad \begin{array}{r} 9 \\ +7 \\ \hline \end{array} \qquad \begin{array}{r} 7 \\ +8 \\ \hline \end{array} \qquad\Big|\qquad \begin{array}{r} 1\,6 \\ -9 \\ \hline \end{array} \qquad \begin{array}{r} 1\,5 \\ -7 \\ \hline \end{array} \qquad \begin{array}{r} 1\,4 \\ -5 \\ \hline \end{array}$$

$$\begin{array}{r} 8 \\ +8 \\ \hline \end{array} \qquad \begin{array}{r} 5 \\ +9 \\ \hline \end{array} \qquad \begin{array}{r} 7 \\ +7 \\ \hline \end{array} \qquad\Big|\qquad \begin{array}{r} 1\,4 \\ -9 \\ \hline \end{array} \qquad \begin{array}{r} 1\,5 \\ -6 \\ \hline \end{array} \qquad \begin{array}{r} 1\,6 \\ -8 \\ \hline \end{array}$$

$$\begin{array}{r} 7 \\ +9 \\ \hline \end{array} \qquad \begin{array}{r} 6 \\ +8 \\ \hline \end{array} \qquad \begin{array}{r} 9 \\ +6 \\ \hline \end{array} \qquad\Big|\qquad \begin{array}{r} 1\,4 \\ -8 \\ \hline \end{array} \qquad \begin{array}{r} 1\,6 \\ -7 \\ \hline \end{array} \qquad \begin{array}{r} 1\,5 \\ -9 \\ \hline \end{array}$$

SPECTRUM MATHEMATICS
Brown Book–Second Edition

Perfect score: 24    My score: _____

# Facts Through 16

## Add.

| | | | | | |
|---|---|---|---|---|---|
| 7<br>+8<br>**15** | 6<br>+6 | 5<br>+9 | 8<br>+4 | 7<br>+7 | 6<br>+9 |
| 8<br>+8 | 9<br>+4 | 7<br>+6 | 8<br>+6 | 7<br>+9 | 8<br>+3 |
| 5<br>+6 | 8<br>+7 | 9<br>+7 | 8<br>+5 | 6<br>+8 | 9<br>+6 |

## Subtract.

| | | | | | |
|---|---|---|---|---|---|
| 14<br>− 7<br>**7** | 15<br>− 6 | 16<br>− 7 | 13<br>− 8 | 14<br>− 5 | 12<br>− 9 |
| 12<br>− 6 | 14<br>− 6 | 11<br>− 9 | 16<br>− 8 | 11<br>− 3 | 15<br>− 9 |
| 15<br>− 7 | 13<br>− 9 | 16<br>− 9 | 14<br>− 9 | 15<br>− 8 | 14<br>− 8 |

SPECTRUM MATHEMATICS,
Brown Book–Second Edition

Perfect score: 36     My score: _____

**Problems**

Solve each problem.

 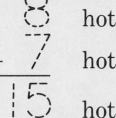

$$
\begin{array}{r}
8 \\
+\ 7 \\
\hline
15
\end{array}
$$

hot dogs in a pack
hot dogs on a tray
hot dogs in all

---

$$
\begin{array}{r}
\phantom{0} \\
+\ \underline{\phantom{0}} \\
\phantom{0}
\end{array}
$$

buns in a pack
more buns
buns in all

---

¢   for a yo-yo
+   ¢   for a top
¢   for both

---

$$
\begin{array}{r}
\phantom{0} \\
+\ \underline{\phantom{0}} \\
\phantom{0}
\end{array}
$$

apples in a bag
other apples
apples in all

---

$$
\begin{array}{r}
\phantom{0} \\
+\ \underline{\phantom{0}} \\
\phantom{0}
\end{array}
$$

books in a box
books in a pile
books in all

SPECTRUM MATHEMATICS,
Brown Book–Second Edition

Perfect score: 5    My score: _____

# Problems

Solve each problem.

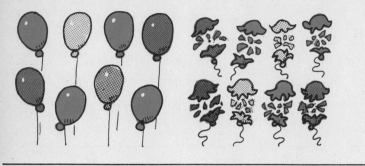

$$\begin{array}{r} 16 \\ -\ 8 \\ \hline 8 \end{array}$$ balloons in all
balloons broken
balloons not broken

_____ cartons in all
− _____ cartons open
_____ cartons closed

_____ rockets in all
− _____ rockets taking off
_____ rockets stay

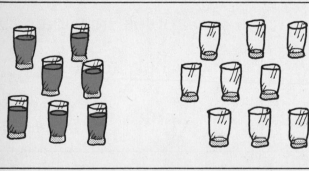

_____ glasses in all
− _____ glasses filled
_____ glasses empty

_____ kites in all
− _____ kites came down
_____ kites still flying

SPECTRUM MATHEMATICS,
Brown Book—Second Edition

Perfect score: 5   My score: _____

NAME _____

## Add or subtract.

$$\begin{array}{r} 9 \\ +8 \\ \hline 17 \end{array} \qquad \begin{array}{r} 8 \\ +9 \\ \hline \end{array} \qquad \begin{array}{r} 17 \\ -8 \\ \hline 9 \end{array} \qquad \begin{array}{r} 17 \\ -9 \\ \hline \end{array}$$

$$\begin{array}{r} 9 \\ +9 \\ \hline \end{array} \qquad \qquad \begin{array}{r} 18 \\ -9 \\ \hline \end{array}$$

$$\begin{array}{r} 6 \\ +8 \\ \hline \end{array} \qquad \begin{array}{r} 8 \\ +8 \\ \hline \end{array} \qquad \begin{array}{r} 8 \\ +9 \\ \hline \end{array} \qquad \begin{array}{r} 17 \\ -8 \\ \hline \end{array} \qquad \begin{array}{r} 15 \\ -7 \\ \hline \end{array} \qquad \begin{array}{r} 16 \\ -9 \\ \hline \end{array}$$

$$\begin{array}{r} 7 \\ +9 \\ \hline \end{array} \qquad \begin{array}{r} 8 \\ +7 \\ \hline \end{array} \qquad \begin{array}{r} 9 \\ +6 \\ \hline \end{array} \qquad \begin{array}{r} 14 \\ -7 \\ \hline \end{array} \qquad \begin{array}{r} 18 \\ -9 \\ \hline \end{array} \qquad \begin{array}{r} 16 \\ -8 \\ \hline \end{array}$$

$$\begin{array}{r} 9 \\ +8 \\ \hline \end{array} \qquad \begin{array}{r} 8 \\ +8 \\ \hline \end{array} \qquad \begin{array}{r} 9 \\ +9 \\ \hline \end{array} \qquad \begin{array}{r} 15 \\ -6 \\ \hline \end{array} \qquad \begin{array}{r} 17 \\ -9 \\ \hline \end{array} \qquad \begin{array}{r} 16 \\ -7 \\ \hline \end{array}$$

# Facts Through 18

## Add.

| | | | | | |
|---|---|---|---|---|---|
| 8<br>+9<br>17 | 9<br>+2 | 5<br>+8 | 9<br>+4 | 6<br>+8 | 5<br>+9 |
| 9<br>+6 | 5<br>+7 | 7<br>+3 | 9<br>+8 | 7<br>+8 | 6<br>+5 |
| 7<br>+7 | 6<br>+6 | 5<br>+5 | 8<br>+8 | 9<br>+9 | 7<br>+9 |

## Subtract.

| | | | | | |
|---|---|---|---|---|---|
| 1 3<br>− 4<br>9 | 1 6<br>− 8 | 1 2<br>− 5 | 1 8<br>− 9 | 1 3<br>− 6 | 1 7<br>− 8 |
| 1 4<br>− 7 | 1 2<br>− 8 | 1 0<br>− 6 | 1 1<br>− 8 | 1 5<br>− 6 | 1 6<br>− 9 |
| 1 7<br>− 9 | 1 4<br>− 5 | 1 6<br>− 7 | 1 5<br>− 8 | 1 2<br>− 6 | 1 5<br>− 7 |

SPECTRUM MATHEMATICS,
Brown Book—Second Edition

Perfect score: 36    My score: _____

**Problems**

Solve each problem.

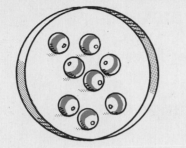 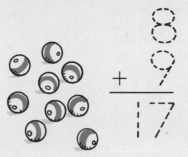

$$\begin{array}{r} 8 \\ + 9 \\ \hline 17 \end{array}$$ beads inside the ring

beads outside the ring

beads in all

___ jars on top shelf

+ ___ jars on bottom shelf

___ jars in all

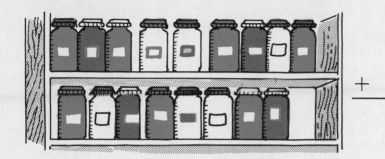

___ pencils in a box

+ ___ more pencils

___ pencils in all

___ big stars

+ ___ small stars

___ stars in all

___ used pencils

+ ___ new pencils

___ pencils in all

SPECTRUM MATHEMATICS,
Brown Book–Second Edition

Perfect score: 5     My score: _____

# Problems

Solve each problem.

17    squares in all

− 8    black squares

9    orange squares

---

_____ worms in all

− _____ worms leave

_____ worms stay

---

_____ bees in all

− _____ bees go away

_____ bees stay

---

_____ balls in all

− _____ small balls

_____ large balls

---

_____ marbles in a bag

− _____ marbles roll out

_____ marbles still in bag

NAME _____

## Add.

|   5   |   7   |   2   |   9   |   5   |   8   |
|-------|-------|-------|-------|-------|-------|
| +7    | +5    | +9    | +2    | +8    | +5    |
| 12    |       |       |       |       |       |

|   6   |   4   |   9   |   4   |   6   |   8   |
|-------|-------|-------|-------|-------|-------|
| +4    | +6    | +4    | +9    | +8    | +6    |

|   7   |   8   |   4   |   8   |   9   |   6   |
|-------|-------|-------|-------|-------|-------|
| +8    | +7    | +8    | +4    | +6    | +9    |

|   7   |   5   |   6   |   5   |   9   |   8   |
|-------|-------|-------|-------|-------|-------|
| +7    | +6    | +5    | +9    | +5    | +8    |

|   5   |   7   |   6   |   9   |   8   |   6   |
|-------|-------|-------|-------|-------|-------|
| +5    | +6    | +7    | +8    | +9    | +6    |

|   7   |   9   |   4   |   8   |   7   |   9   |
|-------|-------|-------|-------|-------|-------|
| +9    | +7    | +8    | +3    | +3    | +9    |

Perfect score: 36    My score: _____

# Addition Facts Through 18

Ring each name for the number in the ⬤.

| | | |
|---|---|---|
| 4 + 8  ⑪  (9 + 2) | | 3 + 8  ⑫  3 + 9 |
| (5 + 6)  6 + 6 | | 6 + 6  6 + 7  8 + 4 |
| (4 + 7)  (8 + 3) | | 7 + 5  5 + 8  5 + 6 |
| 8 + 5  ⑬  7 + 6 | | ⑭  9 + 5 |
| 6 + 8  9 + 5 | | 8 + 6  6 + 7  7 + 7 |
| 9 + 4  6 + 7  4 + 8 | | 6 + 8  8 + 8 |
| 7 + 7  ⑮  9 + 6 | | ⑯  6 + 9 |
| 8 + 7  6 + 9 | | 5 + 7  9 + 7 |
| 5 + 9  7 + 8 | | 8 + 7  7 + 9  8 + 8 |
| ⑰  9 + 9 | | ⑱  4 + 6 |
| 8 + 9  6 + 9 | | 5 + 8  8 + 7 |
| 8 + 8 | | 9 + 9 |
| 8 + 7  9 + 8 | | 6 + 9 |

SPECTRUM MATHEMATICS,
Brown Book–Second Edition

Perfect score: 26    My score: _____

NAME _____

## Subtract.

| | | | | | |
|---|---|---|---|---|---|
| 1 5<br>− 7<br>8 | 1 5<br>− 8 | 1 3<br>− 9 | 1 3<br>− 4 | 1 2<br>− 8 | 1 2<br>− 4 |
| 1 4<br>− 6 | 1 4<br>− 8 | 1 1<br>− 7 | 1 1<br>− 4 | 1 0<br>− 7 | 1 0<br>− 3 |
| 1 5<br>− 6 | 1 5<br>− 9 | 1 4<br>− 9 | 1 4<br>− 5 | 1 7<br>− 8 | 1 7<br>− 9 |
| 1 6<br>− 8 | 1 6<br>− 7 | 1 6<br>− 9 | 1 3<br>− 5 | 1 3<br>− 8 | 1 4<br>− 7 |
| 1 2<br>− 6 | 1 1<br>− 3 | 1 1<br>− 8 | 1 3<br>− 7 | 1 3<br>− 6 | 1 0<br>− 5 |
| 1 0<br>− 8 | 1 0<br>− 2 | 1 2<br>− 5 | 1 2<br>− 7 | 1 8<br>− 9 | 1 5<br>− 7 |

## How many subtraction facts do you know?

| 0 | 1 | 2 | 3 | 4 | 5 | 6 | 7 | 8 | 9 |
|---|---|---|---|---|---|---|---|---|---|
| R | I | U | Y | E | K | O | V | W | N |

Subtract. Write the letter for each answer.

$$\begin{array}{r} 11 \\ -\ 8 \\ \hline \end{array} \quad \begin{array}{r} 15 \\ -\ 9 \\ \hline \end{array} \quad \begin{array}{r} 10 \\ -\ 8 \\ \hline \end{array} \quad \begin{array}{r} 14 \\ -\ 9 \\ \hline \end{array} \quad \begin{array}{r} 16 \\ -\ 7 \\ \hline \end{array} \quad \begin{array}{r} 14 \\ -\ 8 \\ \hline \end{array} \quad \begin{array}{r} 15 \\ -\ 7 \\ \hline \end{array}$$

$$\begin{array}{r} 7 \\ -3 \\ \hline \end{array} \quad \begin{array}{r} 9 \\ -2 \\ \hline \end{array} \quad \begin{array}{r} 8 \\ -4 \\ \hline \end{array} \quad \begin{array}{r} 9 \\ -9 \\ \hline \end{array} \quad \begin{array}{r} 10 \\ -\ 7 \\ \hline \end{array} \quad \begin{array}{r} 11 \\ -\ 5 \\ \hline \end{array} \quad \begin{array}{r} 11 \\ -\ 2 \\ \hline \end{array} \quad \begin{array}{r} 13 \\ -\ 9 \\ \hline \end{array}$$

$$\begin{array}{r} 12 \\ -\ 9 \\ \hline \end{array} \quad \begin{array}{r} 13 \\ -\ 7 \\ \hline \end{array} \quad \begin{array}{r} 11 \\ -\ 9 \\ \hline \end{array} \quad \begin{array}{r} 16 \\ -\ 8 \\ \hline \end{array} \quad \begin{array}{r} 10 \\ -\ 9 \\ \hline \end{array} \quad \begin{array}{r} 18 \\ -\ 9 \\ \hline \end{array}$$

SPECTRUM MATHEMATICS,
Brown Book–Second Edition

Perfect score: 42   My score: _____

**Problems**

NAME _____

Solve each problem.

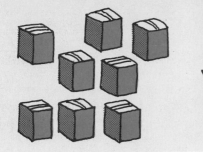 
$$\begin{array}{r} 6 \\ +\ 8 \\ \hline 14 \end{array}$$ 
open boxes
closed boxes
boxes in all

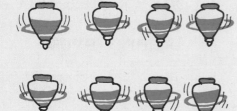
_____ candles in all
$-$ _____ orange candles
_____ white candles

_____ jars in a box
$+$ _____ other jars
_____ jars in all

_____ tops in all
$-$ _____ tops not spinning
_____ tops spinning

_____ acorns on the ground
$+$ _____ acorns falling
_____ acorns in all

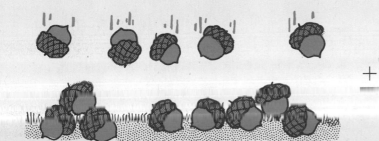

SPECTRUM MATHEMATICS,
Brown Book–Second Edition

Perfect score: 5    My score: _____

49

Add.

| | | | | | |
|---|---|---|---|---|---|
| 9<br>+8 | 5<br>+7 | 8<br>+6 | 7<br>+5 | 4<br>+9 | 5<br>+6 |
| 7<br>+6 | 8<br>+8 | 5<br>+9 | 9<br>+9 | 7<br>+8 | 6<br>+6 |

Subtract.

| | | | | | |
|---|---|---|---|---|---|
| 1 3<br>− 6 | 1 4<br>− 7 | 1 5<br>− 6 | 1 1<br>− 3 | 1 2<br>− 8 | 1 6<br>− 9 |
| 1 3<br>− 8 | 1 2<br>− 9 | 1 1<br>− 5 | 1 7<br>− 8 | 1 8<br>− 9 | 1 5<br>− 7 |

Solve each problem.

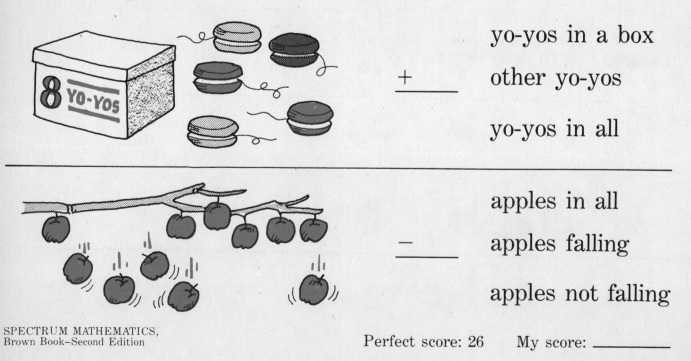

_____ yo-yos in a box

+ _____ other yo-yos

_____ yo-yos in all

_____ apples in all

− _____ apples falling

_____ apples not falling

NAME _____

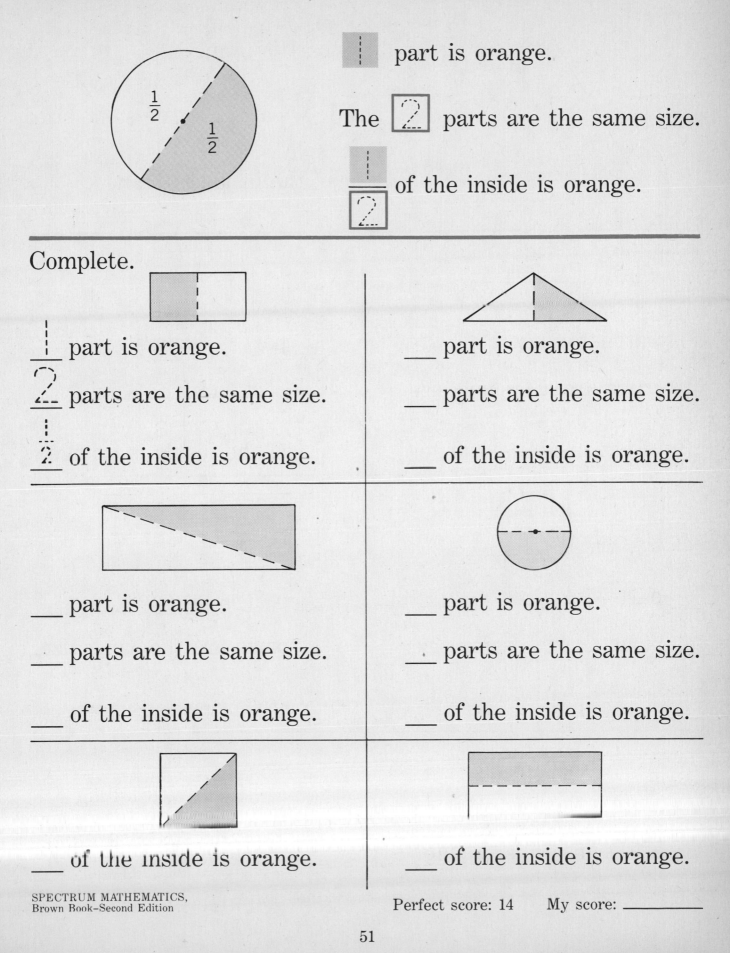

☐ part is orange.

The ☐2☐ parts are the same size.

$\frac{1}{2}$ of the inside is orange.

Complete.

___ part is orange.

___ parts are the same size.

___ of the inside is orange.

___ part is orange.

___ parts are the same size.

___ of the inside is orange.

___ part is orange.

___ parts are the same size.

___ of the inside is orange.

___ part is orange.

___ parts are the same size.

___ of the inside is orange.

___ of the inside is orange.

___ of the inside is orange.

# One Third

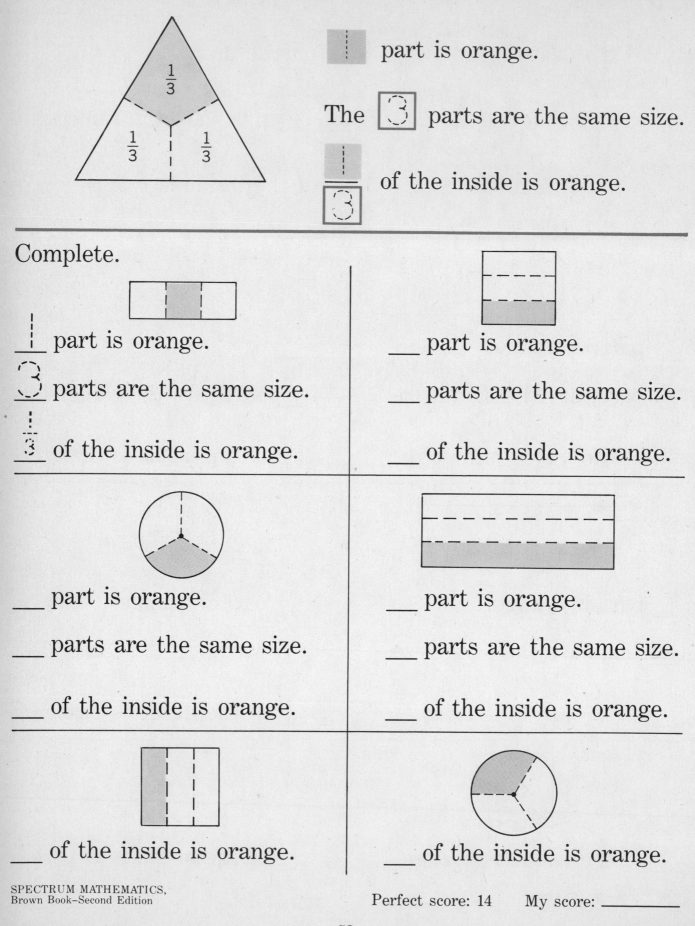

$\frac{1}{3}$  $\frac{1}{3}$  $\frac{1}{3}$

___ part is orange.

The ⟨3⟩ parts are the same size.

$\frac{1}{3}$ of the inside is orange.

Complete.

1 part is orange.

3 parts are the same size.

$\frac{1}{3}$ of the inside is orange.

___ part is orange.

___ parts are the same size.

___ of the inside is orange.

___ part is orange.

___ parts are the same size.

___ of the inside is orange.

___ part is orange.

___ parts are the same size.

___ of the inside is orange.

___ of the inside is orange.

___ of the inside is orange.

NAME _____

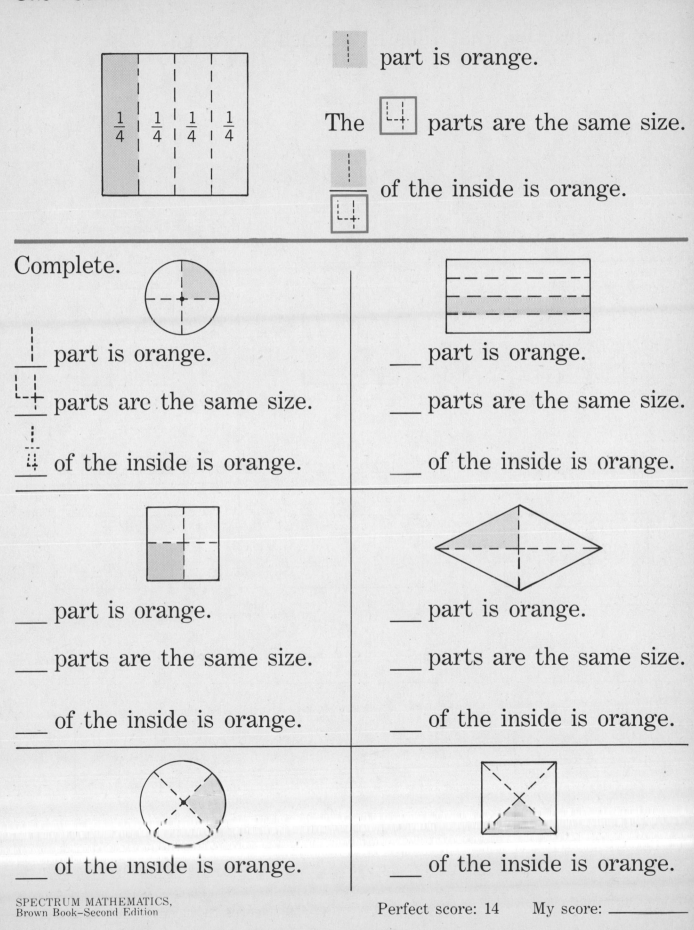

The □ parts are the same size.

___ part is orange.

___ of the inside is orange.

Complete.

___ part is orange.

___ parts are the same size.

___ of the inside is orange.

___ part is orange.

___ parts are the same size.

___ of the inside is orange.

___ part is orange.

___ parts are the same size.

___ of the inside is orange.

___ part is orange.

___ parts are the same size.

___ of the inside is orange.

___ of the inside is orange.

___ of the inside is orange.

# Fractions

Ring the fraction that tells how much is orange.

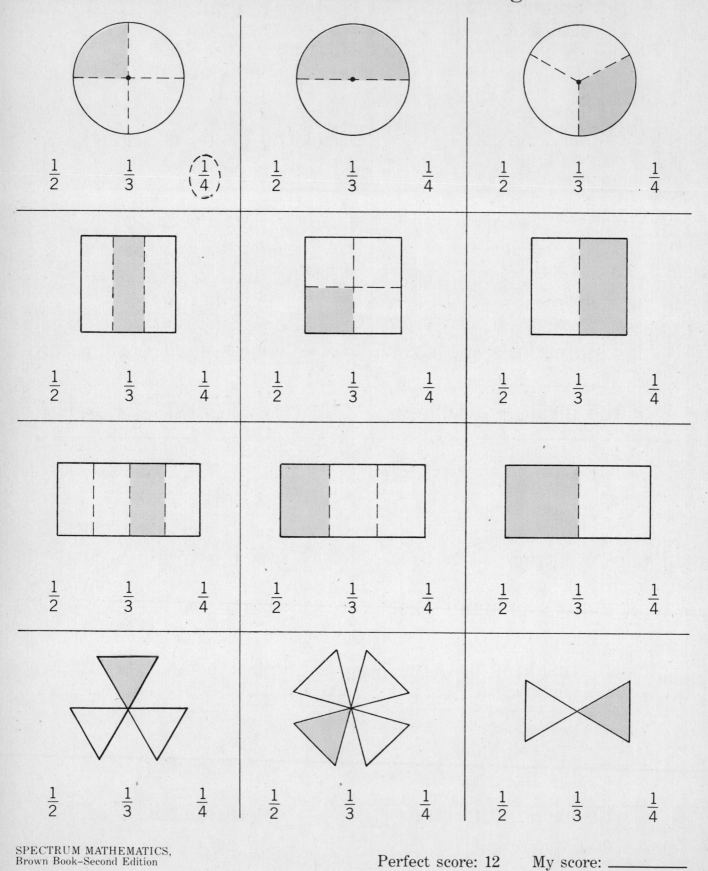

| | | |
|---|---|---|
| $\frac{1}{2}$ $\frac{1}{3}$ $\left(\frac{1}{4}\right)$ | $\frac{1}{2}$ $\frac{1}{3}$ $\frac{1}{4}$ | $\frac{1}{2}$ $\frac{1}{3}$ $\frac{1}{4}$ |
| $\frac{1}{2}$ $\frac{1}{3}$ $\frac{1}{4}$ | $\frac{1}{2}$ $\frac{1}{3}$ $\frac{1}{4}$ | $\frac{1}{2}$ $\frac{1}{3}$ $\frac{1}{4}$ |
| $\frac{1}{2}$ $\frac{1}{3}$ $\frac{1}{4}$ | $\frac{1}{2}$ $\frac{1}{3}$ $\frac{1}{4}$ | $\frac{1}{2}$ $\frac{1}{3}$ $\frac{1}{4}$ |
| $\frac{1}{2}$ $\frac{1}{3}$ $\frac{1}{4}$ | $\frac{1}{2}$ $\frac{1}{3}$ $\frac{1}{4}$ | $\frac{1}{2}$ $\frac{1}{3}$ $\frac{1}{4}$ |

SPECTRUM MATHEMATICS,
Brown Book–Second Edition

Perfect score: 12     My score: _____

NAME _____

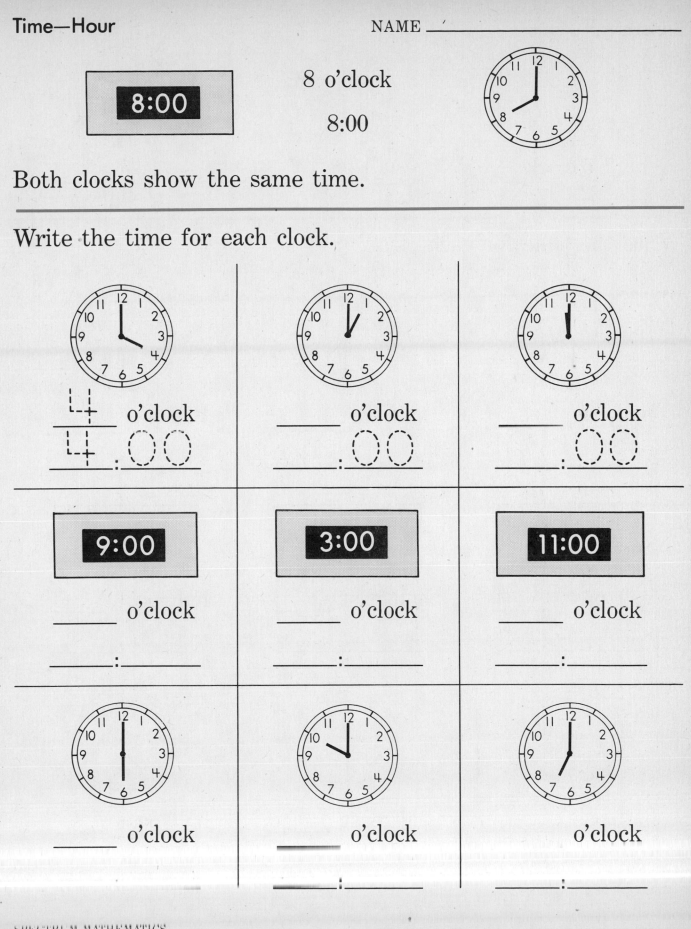

8 o'clock

8:00

**8:00**

Both clocks show the same time.

Write the time for each clock.

4 o'clock

4:00

_____ o'clock

_____.00

_____ o'clock

_____.00

**9:00**

_____ o'clock

_____ : _____

**3:00**

_____ o'clock

_____ : _____

**11:00**

_____ o'clock

_____ : _____

_____ o'clock

_____ : _____

_____ o'clock

_____ : _____

_____ o'clock

_____ : _____

2 o'clock
2:00

half past 2
2:30

3 o'clock
3:00

Write the time for each clock.

half past 3
3:30

half past ___
___:30

half past ___
___:30

10:30

half past ___
___:___

4:30

half past ___
___:___

7:30

half past ___
___:___

half past ___
___:___

half past ___
___:___

half past ___
___:___

Perfect score: 18    My score: _____

# Time

## Show this time on this clock.    ## Show this time on this clock.

**Checkup**

# Ring the fraction that tells how much is orange.

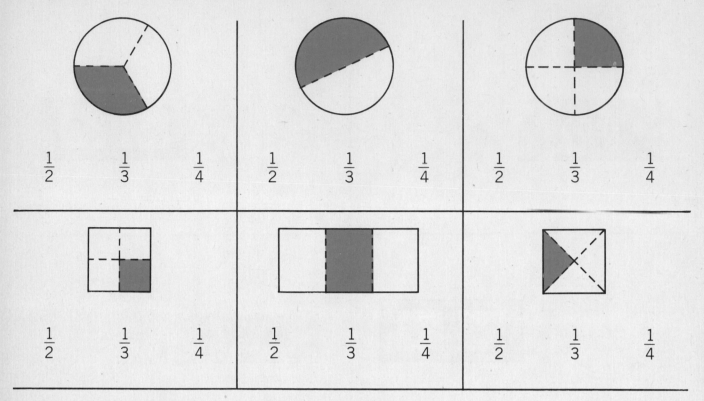

$\frac{1}{2}$    $\frac{1}{3}$    $\frac{1}{4}$

$\frac{1}{2}$    $\frac{1}{3}$    $\frac{1}{4}$

$\frac{1}{2}$    $\frac{1}{3}$    $\frac{1}{4}$

$\frac{1}{2}$    $\frac{1}{3}$    $\frac{1}{4}$

$\frac{1}{2}$    $\frac{1}{3}$    $\frac{1}{4}$

$\frac{1}{2}$    $\frac{1}{3}$    $\frac{1}{4}$

# Write the time for each clock.

half past _____

_____ o'clock

_____ : _____

_____ : _____

_____ : _____

_____ : _____

SPECTRUM MATHEMATICS,
Brown Book–Second Edition

Perfect score: 12    My score: _____

# Addition and Subtraction

## Add.

| | | | | | |
|---|---|---|---|---|---|
| 2<br>+2 | 3<br>+6 | 7<br>+1 | 5<br>+3 | 4<br>+2 | 1<br>+6 |
| 8<br>+2 | 7<br>+4 | 3<br>+9 | 6<br>+6 | 8<br>+9 | 7<br>+6 |
| 8<br>+5 | 9<br>+9 | 6<br>+4 | 7<br>+8 | 4<br>+9 | 7<br>+9 |

## Subtract.

| | | | | | |
|---|---|---|---|---|---|
| 5<br>−4 | 7<br>−5 | 8<br>−8 | 9<br>−8 | 6<br>−3 | 8<br>−2 |
| 11<br>− 9 | 10<br>− 3 | 12<br>− 6 | 14<br>− 8 | 16<br>− 9 | 12<br>− 5 |
| 13<br>− 6 | 16<br>− 8 | 17<br>− 9 | 10<br>− 8 | 14<br>− 7 | 15<br>− 7 |

SPECTRUM MATHEMATICS,
Brown Book–Second Edition

Perfect score: 36    My score: _____

# Addition and Subtraction

Add or subtract.

If you get 9, color the part red.
If you get 14, color the part brown.

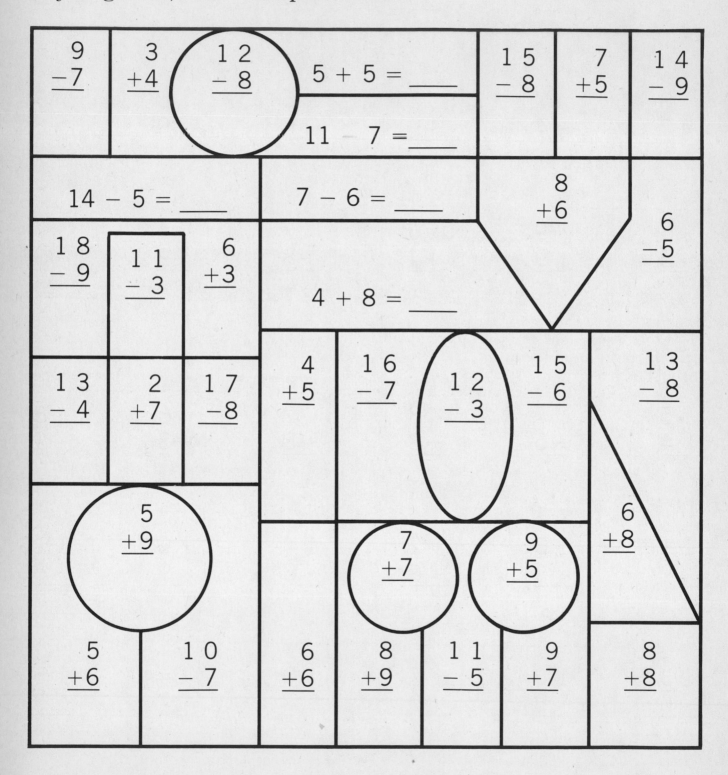

# Adding Tens

```
  3 tens          3 0              5 tens          5 0
+ 4 tens        + 4 0            + 3 tens        + 3 0
  7 tens          7 0              8 tens          80
```

---

Add.

```
  1 ten           1 0              7 tens          7 0
+ 3 tens        + 3 0            + 2 tens        + 2 0
    tens                             tens
```

```
  1 0             6 0              2 0             2 0             4 0
+ 1 0           + 1 0            + 1 0           + 6 0           + 5 0
```

```
  3 0             2 0             4 0              5 0             1 0
+ 2 0           + 3 0           + 4 0            + 1 0           + 5 0
```

```
  4 0             2 0             6 0              5 0             8 0
+ 1 0           + 2 0           + 3 0            + 2 0           + 1 0
```

```
  3 0             6 0             3 0              2 0             1 0
+ 3 0           + 2 0           + 5 0            + 4 0           + 7 0
```

# Addition (2 digit)

$$\begin{array}{r} 32 \\ +14 \\ \hline 6 \end{array}$$
⟹
$$\begin{array}{r} 32 \\ +14 \\ \hline 46 \end{array}$$

---

## Add.

$$\begin{array}{r} 58 \\ +\ 1 \\ \hline 59 \end{array}$$
↑ — Add the ones.
↑ — Add the tens.

$$\begin{array}{r} 47 \\ +32 \\ \hline 79 \end{array}$$

$$\begin{array}{r} 70 \\ +16 \\ \hline \end{array}$$

$$\begin{array}{r} 26 \\ +52 \\ \hline \end{array}$$

$$\begin{array}{r} 23 \\ +24 \\ \hline \end{array}$$

$$\begin{array}{r} 64 \\ +25 \\ \hline \end{array}$$

$$\begin{array}{r} 54 \\ +\ 4 \\ \hline \end{array}$$

$$\begin{array}{r} 47 \\ +11 \\ \hline \end{array}$$

$$\begin{array}{r} 34 \\ +30 \\ \hline \end{array}$$

$$\begin{array}{r} 12 \\ +13 \\ \hline \end{array}$$

$$\begin{array}{r} 41 \\ +23 \\ \hline \end{array}$$

$$\begin{array}{r} 26 \\ +\ 3 \\ \hline \end{array}$$

$$\begin{array}{r} 80 \\ +17 \\ \hline \end{array}$$

$$\begin{array}{r} 23 \\ +75 \\ \hline \end{array}$$

$$\begin{array}{r} 40 \\ +30 \\ \hline \end{array}$$

$$\begin{array}{r} 52 \\ +26 \\ \hline \end{array}$$

$$\begin{array}{r} 91 \\ +\ 5 \\ \hline \end{array}$$

$$\begin{array}{r} 43 \\ +46 \\ \hline \end{array}$$

$$\begin{array}{r} 33 \\ +26 \\ \hline \end{array}$$

$$\begin{array}{r} 52 \\ +34 \\ \hline \end{array}$$

$$\begin{array}{r} 84 \\ +12 \\ \hline \end{array}$$

$$\begin{array}{r} 62 \\ +\ 7 \\ \hline \end{array}$$

$$\begin{array}{r} 53 \\ +41 \\ \hline \end{array}$$

$$\begin{array}{r} 71 \\ +27 \\ \hline \end{array}$$

Add.

| | | | | |
|---|---|---|---|---|
| 3 2<br>+2 7<br>**5 9** | 5 1<br>+ 6<br>**5 7** | 3 0<br>+1 0 | 1 2<br>+1 2 | 6 4<br>+2 1 |
| 3 6<br>+3 3 | 1 2<br>+ 4 | 2 4<br>+1 3 | 7 0<br>+1 3 | 5 4<br>+3 5 |
| 5 5<br>+2 1 | 8 1<br>+ 8 | 4 2<br>+4 3 | 7 1<br>+2 3 | 6 2<br>+1 6 |
| 1 1<br>+4 1 | 6 5<br>+ 4 | 4 1<br>+2 2 | 2 3<br>+2 6 | 4 9<br>+4 0 |
| 3 1<br>+4 7 | 4 3<br>+ 5 | 2 7<br>+5 1 | 8 3<br>+1 2 | 1 2<br>+5 7 |
| 4 3<br>+5 1 | 7 2<br>+ 7 | 1 0<br>+6 2 | 5 3<br>+3 6 | 7 3<br>+2 5 |

## Problems

| Ken has | Jill has | Pam has | Rod has |
|---|---|---|---|
| 25¢ | 26¢ | 20¢ | 32¢ |

Complete.

Who has the most money? _____

Who has the least money? _____

Solve each problem.

| | | | |
|---|---|---|---|
| Ken has | 25¢ | Pam has | 20¢ |
| Pam has | +20¢ | Rod has | +32¢ |
| Ken and Pam have | 45¢ | Pam and Rod have | ¢ |

| | | | |
|---|---|---|---|
| Jill has | ¢ | Rod has | ¢ |
| Pam has | + ___ ¢ | Jill has | + ___ ¢ |
| Jill and Pam have | ¢ | Rod and Jill have | ¢ |

| | | | |
|---|---|---|---|
| Ken has | ¢ | Pam has | ¢ |
| Rod has | + ___ ¢ | Ken has | + ___ ¢ |
| Ken and Rod have | ¢ | Pam and Ken have | ¢ |

SPECTRUM MATHEMATICS,
Brown Book–Second Edition

Perfect score: 8    My score: _____

## Subtracting Tens

| 7 tens | 7 0 | | 9 tens | 9 0 |
|--------|-----|--|--------|-----|
| −4 tens | −4 0 | | −1 ten | −1 0 |
| 3 tens | 3 0 | | 8 tens | 80 |

Subtract.

| 5 tens | 5 0 | | 3 tens | 3 0 |
|--------|-----|--|--------|-----|
| −3 tens | −3 0 | | −1 ten | −1 0 |
| tens | | | tens | |

| 4 0 | 8 0 | 5 0 | 9 0 | 7 0 |
|-----|-----|-----|-----|-----|
| −3 0 | −6 0 | −1 0 | −6 0 | −2 0 |

| 2 0 | 4 0 | 3 0 | 5 0 | 6 0 |
|-----|-----|-----|-----|-----|
| −1 0 | −2 0 | −2 0 | −4 0 | −3 0 |

| 7 0 | 7 0 | 6 0 | 6 0 | 4 0 |
|-----|-----|-----|-----|-----|
| −1 0 | −6 0 | −2 0 | −4 0 | −1 0 |

| 9 0 | 8 0 | 6 0 | 8 0 | 9 0 |
|-----|-----|-----|-----|-----|
| −4 0 | −3 0 | −5 0 | −4 0 | −7 0 |

# Subtraction (2 digit)

Take away **1** penny.
Subtract the ones.

$$\begin{array}{r} 53 \\ -21 \\ \hline 2 \end{array}$$

Take away **2** dimes.
Subtract the tens.

$$\begin{array}{r} 53 \\ -21 \\ \hline 32 \end{array}$$

## Subtract.

$$\begin{array}{r} 79 \\ -\ 6 \\ \hline 73 \end{array}$$

↑ └ Subtract the ones.
  └ Subtract the tens.

$$\begin{array}{r} 82 \\ -52 \\ \hline 30 \end{array}$$

$$\begin{array}{r} 65 \\ -24 \\ \hline \end{array}$$

$$\begin{array}{r} 56 \\ -26 \\ \hline \end{array}$$

$$\begin{array}{r} 87 \\ -23 \\ \hline \end{array}$$

$$\begin{array}{r} 36 \\ -20 \\ \hline \end{array}$$

$$\begin{array}{r} 94 \\ -\ 1 \\ \hline \end{array}$$

$$\begin{array}{r} 58 \\ -17 \\ \hline \end{array}$$

$$\begin{array}{r} 65 \\ -51 \\ \hline \end{array}$$

$$\begin{array}{r} 57 \\ -10 \\ \hline \end{array}$$

$$\begin{array}{r} 89 \\ -64 \\ \hline \end{array}$$

$$\begin{array}{r} 46 \\ -\ 3 \\ \hline \end{array}$$

$$\begin{array}{r} 75 \\ -15 \\ \hline \end{array}$$

$$\begin{array}{r} 37 \\ -24 \\ \hline \end{array}$$

$$\begin{array}{r} 46 \\ -34 \\ \hline \end{array}$$

$$\begin{array}{r} 78 \\ -68 \\ \hline \end{array}$$

$$\begin{array}{r} 29 \\ -\ 2 \\ \hline \end{array}$$

$$\begin{array}{r} 85 \\ -43 \\ \hline \end{array}$$

$$\begin{array}{r} 78 \\ -21 \\ \hline \end{array}$$

$$\begin{array}{r} 79 \\ -61 \\ \hline \end{array}$$

$$\begin{array}{r} 97 \\ -65 \\ \hline \end{array}$$

$$\begin{array}{r} 84 \\ -\ 2 \\ \hline \end{array}$$

$$\begin{array}{r} 65 \\ -22 \\ \hline \end{array}$$

$$\begin{array}{r} 99 \\ -37 \\ \hline \end{array}$$

SPECTRUM MATHEMATICS,
Brown Book–Second Edition

Perfect score: 24   My score: _____

## Subtraction (2 digit)

Subtract.

| | | | | |
|---|---|---|---|---|
| 62<br>−31<br>**31** | 88<br>− 6<br>**82** | 69<br>−15 | 34<br>−13 | 84<br>−12 |
| 57<br>−24 | 15<br>− 1 | 79<br>−21 | 96<br>−81 | 88<br>−23 |
| 98<br>−50 | 77<br>− 3 | 88<br>−14 | 65<br>−24 | 79<br>−59 |
| 66<br>−54 | 49<br>− 3 | 87<br>−57 | 97<br>−85 | 59<br>−32 |
| 84<br>−74 | 29<br>− 6 | 47<br>−11 | 39<br>−27 | 84<br>−31 |
| 75<br>−61 | 98<br>− 2 | 73<br>−32 | 85<br>−43 | 99<br>−64 |

SPECTRUM MATHEMATICS,
Brown Book–Second Edition

Perfect score: 30   My score: _____

# Problems

| Maria has | John has | Renee has | Dan has |
|---|---|---|---|

| 35¢ | 45¢ | 12¢ | 24¢ |
|---|---|---|---|

Solve each problem.

John has      45¢

Maria has     − 35¢

John has this
much more.     10¢

Dan has      24¢

Renee has     − 12¢

Dan has this
much more.     ¢

---

John has       ¢

Dan has      − ¢

John has this
much more.     ¢

Maria has      ¢

Dan has      − ¢

Maria has this
much more.     ¢

---

Maria has      ¢

Renee has     − ¢

Maria has this
much more.     ¢

John has       ¢

Renee has     − ¢

John has this
much more.     ¢

SPECTRUM MATHEMATICS,
Brown Book—Second Edition

Perfect score: 6    My score: _____

# Adding Three Numbers

Add the ones.                              Add the tens.

$$\begin{array}{r} 12 \\ 53 \\ +24 \\ \hline 9 \end{array} \rightarrow 5 \\ +4$$

$$\begin{array}{r} 60 \\ +20 \\ \hline 89 \end{array} \leftarrow \begin{array}{r} 12 \\ 53 \\ +24 \end{array}$$

## Add.

| 1. | 2. | 3. | 4. | 5. | 6. |
|---|---|---|---|---|---|
| $\begin{array}{r} 1 \\ 6 \\ +1 \\ \hline 8 \end{array}$ | $\begin{array}{r} 2 \\ 4 \\ +2 \\ \hline \end{array}$ | $\begin{array}{r} 3 \\ 5 \\ +0 \\ \hline \end{array}$ | $\begin{array}{r} 4 \\ 1 \\ +4 \\ \hline \end{array}$ | $\begin{array}{r} 2 \\ 2 \\ +5 \\ \hline \end{array}$ | $\begin{array}{r} 3 \\ 3 \\ +3 \\ \hline \end{array}$ |
| $\begin{array}{r} 30 \\ 10 \\ +10 \\ \hline 50 \end{array}$ | $\begin{array}{r} 20 \\ 30 \\ +10 \\ \hline \end{array}$ | $\begin{array}{r} 20 \\ 20 \\ +20 \\ \hline \end{array}$ | $\begin{array}{r} 30 \\ 20 \\ +0 \\ \hline \end{array}$ | $\begin{array}{r} 40 \\ 30 \\ +10 \\ \hline \end{array}$ | |
| $\begin{array}{r} 31 \\ 16 \\ +11 \\ \hline 58 \end{array}$ | $\begin{array}{r} 14 \\ 10 \\ +11 \\ \hline \end{array}$ | $\begin{array}{r} 66 \\ 20 \\ +13 \\ \hline \end{array}$ | $\begin{array}{r} 15 \\ 51 \\ +1 \\ \hline \end{array}$ | $\begin{array}{r} 41 \\ 14 \\ +12 \\ \hline \end{array}$ | |
| $\begin{array}{r} 33 \\ 21 \\ +23 \\ \hline \end{array}$ | $\begin{array}{r} 31 \\ 12 \\ +51 \\ \hline \end{array}$ | $\begin{array}{r} 54 \\ 12 \\ +21 \\ \hline \end{array}$ | $\begin{array}{r} 71 \\ 17 \\ +1 \\ \hline \end{array}$ | $\begin{array}{r} 32 \\ 21 \\ +32 \\ \hline \end{array}$ | |

# Adding Three Numbers

## Why did the bird fly south?

| A | F | I | K | L | O | R | S | T | W |
|---|---|----|----|----|----|----|----|----|----|
| 7 | 9 | 35 | 39 | 47 | 58 | 59 | 68 | 86 | 88 |

Add. Write the letter for each answer.

$$
\begin{array}{r} 1\,2 \\ 1\,2 \\ +1\,1 \\ \hline 35 \end{array}
\qquad
\begin{array}{r} 4\,3 \\ 2\,2 \\ +2\,1 \\ \hline \end{array}
\qquad\qquad\qquad
\begin{array}{r} 3\,0 \\ 2\,4 \\ +3\,4 \\ \hline \end{array}
\qquad
\begin{array}{r} 3 \\ 2 \\ +2 \\ \hline \end{array}
\qquad
\begin{array}{r} 2\,5 \\ 3\,1 \\ +1\,2 \\ \hline \end{array}
$$

I    ☐        ☐    ☐    ☐

$$
\begin{array}{r} 5\,1 \\ 2\,4 \\ +1\,1 \\ \hline \end{array}
\qquad
\begin{array}{r} 1\,6 \\ 2\,0 \\ +2\,2 \\ \hline \end{array}
\qquad
\begin{array}{r} 3\,1 \\ 1\,6 \\ +1\,1 \\ \hline \end{array}
\qquad\qquad
\begin{array}{r} 3 \\ 3 \\ +3 \\ \hline \end{array}
\qquad
\begin{array}{r} 1 \\ 2 \\ +4 \\ \hline \end{array}
\qquad
\begin{array}{r} 1\,3 \\ 2\,4 \\ +2\,2 \\ \hline \end{array}
$$

☐    ☐    ☐        ☐    ☐    ☐

$$
\begin{array}{r} 6\,3 \\ 1\,0 \\ +1\,3 \\ \hline \end{array}
\qquad
\begin{array}{r} 3\,0 \\ 1\,7 \\ +1\,1 \\ \hline \end{array}
\qquad\qquad
\begin{array}{r} 5\,1 \\ 2\,6 \\ +1\,1 \\ \hline \end{array}
\qquad
\begin{array}{r} 3 \\ 3 \\ +1 \\ \hline \end{array}
\qquad
\begin{array}{r} 1\,4 \\ 2\,3 \\ +1\,0 \\ \hline \end{array}
\qquad
\begin{array}{r} 1\,3 \\ 1\,1 \\ +1\,5 \\ \hline \end{array}
$$

☐    ☐        ☐    ☐    ☐    ☐

SPECTRUM MATHEMATICS,
Brown Book–Second Edition

Perfect score: 34    My score: _____

**Money**

half dollar

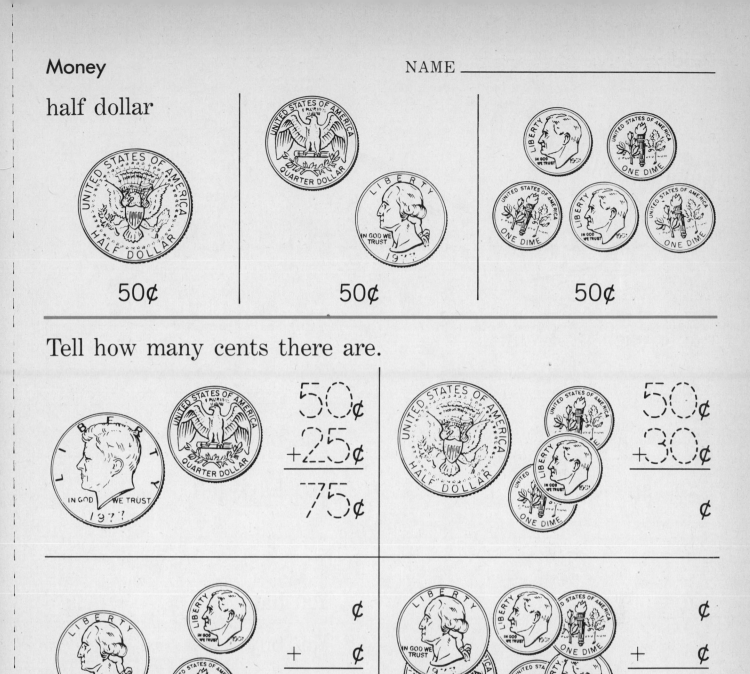

| 50¢ | 50¢ | 50¢ |

Tell how many cents there are.

$$\begin{array}{r} 50¢ \\ +25¢ \\ \hline 75¢ \end{array}$$

$$\begin{array}{r} 50¢ \\ +30¢ \\ \hline \quad¢ \end{array}$$

$$\begin{array}{r} \quad¢ \\ +\quad¢ \\ \hline \quad¢ \end{array}$$

$$\begin{array}{r} \quad¢ \\ +\quad¢ \\ \hline \quad¢ \end{array}$$

$$\begin{array}{r} 50¢ \\ 25¢ \\ +10¢ \\ \hline \quad¢ \end{array}$$

$$\begin{array}{r} \quad¢ \\ \quad¢ \\ +\quad¢ \\ \hline \quad¢ \end{array}$$

# Problems

Comb price tag: 30¢  Toothbrush price tag: 34¢  Tooth Paste price tag: 25¢

---

Solve each problem.

| You buy a (comb) | $30$¢ | You have | $50$¢ |
| and a (toothbrush). | $+34$¢ | You buy a (comb). | $-30$¢ |
| You spent | ¢ | You have left | ¢ |

| You buy a (toothbrush) | ¢ | You have | $89$¢ |
| and (Tooth Paste). | $+$ ¢ | You buy a (Tooth Paste). | $-$ ¢ |
| You spent | ¢ | You have left | ¢ |

| You buy a (comb) | ¢ | You have | $97$¢ |
| and (Tooth Paste). | $+$ ¢ | You buy a (toothbrush). | $-$ ¢ |
| You spent | ¢ | You have left | ¢ |

SPECTRUM MATHEMATICS,
Brown Book–Second Edition

Perfect score: 6    My score: _____

## Addition and Subtraction

NAME _____

Add.

| | | | | | |
|---|---|---|---|---|---|
| 3 6 | 5 4 | 1 6 | 4 0 | 6 1 | 7 5 |
| +2 1 | +3 5 | + 2 | + 5 | +1 8 | +2 2 |

| | | | | | |
|---|---|---|---|---|---|
| 3 1 | 2 6 | 3 4 | 9 2 | 4 3 | 5 1 |
| +1 7 | +4 0 | + 4 | + 2 | +3 3 | +1 4 |

| | | | | | |
|---|---|---|---|---|---|
| 1 2 | 3 0 | 1 8 | 5 1 | 3 5 | 4 3 |
| 1 3 | 2 4 | 2 0 | 6 | 2 2 | 2 0 |
| +1 4 | +4 2 | + 1 | + 2 | +2 2 | +2 6 |

Subtract.

| | | | | | |
|---|---|---|---|---|---|
| 8 9 | 6 6 | 8 7 | 4 8 | 6 7 | 7 8 |
| −1 3 | −4 3 | − 1 | − 6 | −1 0 | −6 5 |

| | | | | | |
|---|---|---|---|---|---|
| 5 8 | 9 1 | 6 7 | 9 5 | 8 7 | 9 9 |
| −3 4 | −4 1 | − 3 | − 2 | −7 7 | −1 2 |

**Checkup**

## Add.

```
  4 3        6 1        8 3        5 9        7 2        3 4
+   4      +   5      + 1 6      + 4 0      + 2 2      + 5 4
```

```
  4          2 6        3 1        4 2        5 7        3 3
  3          1 2        4 0        3 5        2 1        2 2
+ 2        +   1      + 1 8      + 2 1      + 1 1      + 1 2
```

## Subtract.

```
  2 3        7 4        8 5        9 2        6 8        7 9
-   1      -   3      - 5 2      - 2 2      - 3 7      - 3 1
```

```
  3 9        4 7        5 6        7 5        8 1        9 6
-   4      -   6      - 3 4      - 4 0      - 4 1      - 3 5
```

---

## Solve each problem.

| | |
|---|---|
| Paul had 31¢. | ____ ¢ |
| He spent 21¢. | − ____ ¢ |
| Paul has this much left. | ____ ¢ |

| | |
|---|---|
| June had 48¢. | ____ ¢ |
| She spent 23¢. | − ____ ¢ |
| June has this much left. | ____ ¢ |

SPECTRUM MATHEMATICS,
Brown Book–Second Edition

Perfect score: 26     My score: _____

NAME _____

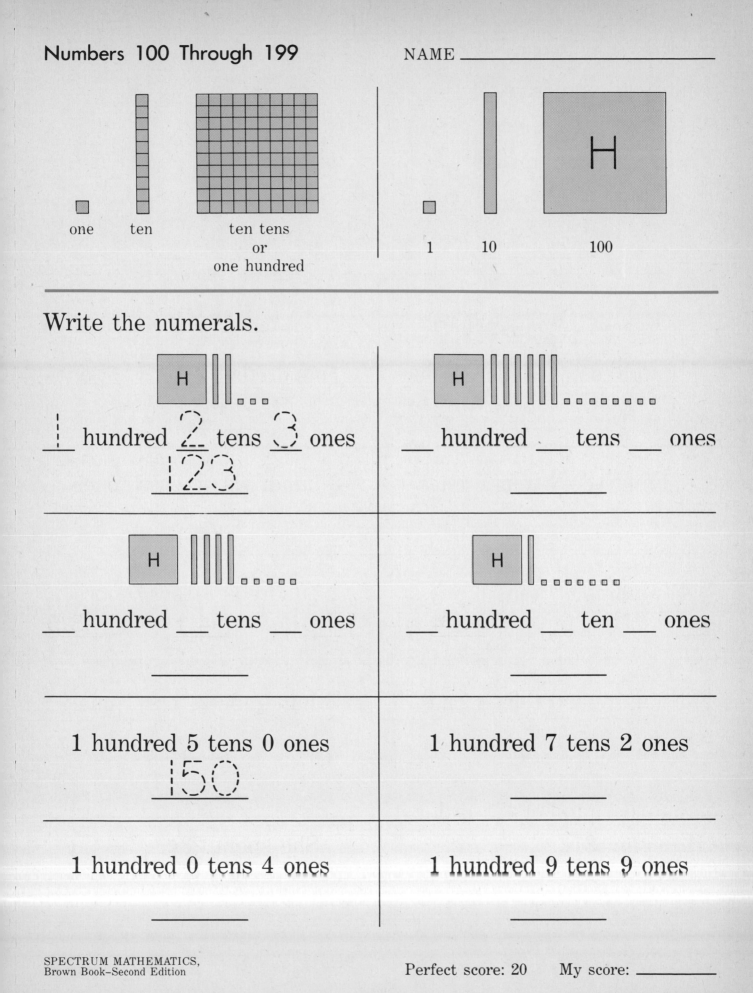

Write the numerals.

1 hundred 2 tens 3 ones

123

___ hundred ___ tens ___ ones

_____

___ hundred ___ tens ___ ones

_____

___ hundred ___ ten ___ ones

_____

1 hundred 5 tens 0 ones

150

1 hundred 7 tens 2 ones

_____

1 hundred 0 tens 4 ones

_____

1 hundred 9 tens 9 ones

_____

## Write the numerals.

<u>2</u> hundreds <u>7</u> tens <u>9</u> ones

279

<u>4</u> hundreds <u>3</u> tens <u>0</u> ones

_____

___ hundreds ___ tens ___ ones

_____

___ hundreds ___ tens ___ ones

_____

2 hundreds 3 tens 6 ones

_____

3 hundreds 4 tens 0 ones

_____

4 hundreds 9 tens 9 ones

_____

2 hundreds 8 tens 9 ones

_____

4 hundreds 0 tens 4 ones

_____

3 hundreds 2 tens 1 one

_____

## Name the numbers in order.

265, 266, _____, _____, _____, _____, _____

398, 399, _____, _____, _____, _____, _____

SPECTRUM MATHEMATICS,
Brown Book–Second Edition

Perfect score: 34    My score: _____

NAME _____

# Write the numerals.

| | | | | | | | | | | |
|---|---|---|---|---|---|---|---|---|---|---|
| H | H | H | H | H ||| H | H | H | H | H | H |

5 hundreds 2 tens 0 ones         ___ hundreds ___ tens ___ ones

_____                                    _____

6 hundreds 2 tens 1 one          7 hundreds 1 ten 4 ones

_____                                    _____

5 hundreds 5 tens 3 ones         6 hundreds 9 tens 7 ones

_____                                    _____

6 hundreds 7 tens 8 ones         7 hundreds 3 tens 2 ones

_____                                    _____

7 hundreds 6 tens 5 ones         5 hundreds 8 tens 3 ones

_____                                    _____

6 hundreds 1 ten 0 ones          7 hundreds 7 tens 6 ones

_____                                    _____

7 hundreds 9 tens 9 ones         5 hundreds 8 tens 8 ones

_____                                    _____

SPECTRUM MATHEMATICS,
Brown Book–Second Edition                    Perfect score: 20    My score: _____

Write the numerals.

8 hundreds 2 tens 5 ones

_____

___ hundreds ___ ten ___ ones

_____

9 hundreds 2 tens 8 ones

_____

8 hundreds 4 tens 2 ones

_____

8 hundreds 9 tens 2 ones

_____

9 hundreds 0 tens 3 ones

_____

9 hundreds 7 tens 5 ones

_____

8 hundreds 4 tens 0 ones

_____

Count by hundreds to complete the row.

100, 200, _____, _____, _____, _____, _____, _____, 900

Count by tens to complete the row.

850, 860, _____, _____, _____, _____, _____, _____, _____

Write the numerals.

| | |
|---|---|
| 8 hundreds 6 tens 4 ones | 5 hundreds 3 tens 8 ones |
| _____ | _____ |
| 3 hundreds 1 ten 5 ones | 9 hundreds 8 tens 3 ones |
| _____ | _____ |
| 1 hundred 0 tens 1 one | 4 hundreds 2 tens 7 ones |
| _____ | _____ |

Start at 780.
Connect the dots in order.

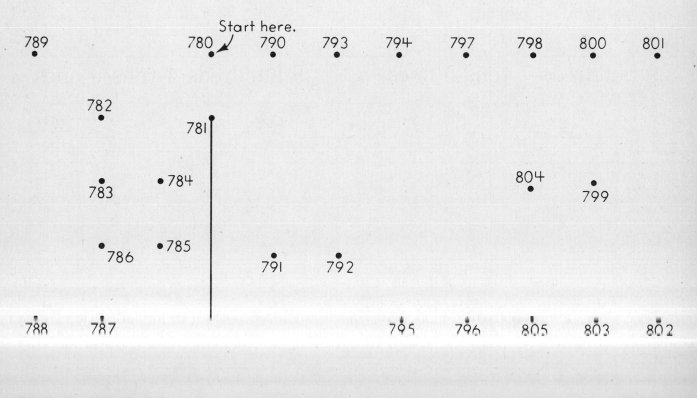

# Numbers 100 Through 999

Complete.

| After | Between | Before |
|---|---|---|
| 419, _420_ | 818, _819_, 820 | _770_, 771 |
| 301, _____ | 324, _____, 326 | _____, 346 |
| 143, _____ | 606, _____, 608 | _____, 160 |
| 854, _____ | 255, _____, 257 | _____, 200 |
| 209, _____ | 172, _____, 174 | _____, 423 |
| 688, _____ | 760, _____, 762 | _____, 950 |
| 579, _____ | 939, _____, 941 | _____, 667 |
| 993, _____ | 499, _____, 501 | _____, 181 |
| 629, _____ | 847, _____, 849 | _____, 800 |
| 799, _____ | 583, _____, 585 | _____, 595 |

SPECTRUM MATHEMATICS,
Brown Book–Second Edition

Perfect score: 30     My score: _____

# Adding Hundreds

| 6 hundreds | 600 | | 3 hundreds | 300 |
|---|---|---|---|---|
| +2 hundreds | +200 | | +4 hundreds | +400 |
| 8 hundreds | 800 | | 7 hundreds | 700 |

## Add.

| 2 hundreds | 200 | | 5 hundreds | 500 |
|---|---|---|---|---|
| +1 hundred | +100 | | +3 hundreds | +300 |
| hundreds | | | hundreds | |

| 100 | 100 | 700 | 400 |
|---|---|---|---|
| +100 | +800 | +100 | +500 |

| 300 | 300 | 100 | 400 |
|---|---|---|---|
| +200 | +600 | +300 | +400 |

| 600 | 200 | 400 | 300 |
|---|---|---|---|
| +100 | +500 | +100 | +300 |

| 100 | 400 | 200 | 700 |
|---|---|---|---|
| +500 | +200 | +200 | +200 |

## Addition (3 digit)

Add the ones.

$$\begin{array}{r} 356 \\ +341 \\ \hline 7 \end{array}$$

Add the tens.

$$\begin{array}{r} 356 \\ +341 \\ \hline 97 \end{array}$$

Add the hundreds.

$$\begin{array}{r} 356 \\ +341 \\ \hline 697 \end{array}$$

## Add.

$$\begin{array}{r} 862 \\ +\ 13 \\ \hline 875 \end{array}$$

Add the ones.
Add the tens.
Add the hundreds.

$$\begin{array}{r} 715 \\ +104 \\ \hline \end{array}$$

Add the ones.
Add the tens.
Add the hundreds.

$$\begin{array}{r} 246 \\ +353 \\ \hline \end{array}$$
$$\begin{array}{r} 394 \\ +400 \\ \hline \end{array}$$
$$\begin{array}{r} 815 \\ +\ 42 \\ \hline \end{array}$$
$$\begin{array}{r} 170 \\ +217 \\ \hline \end{array}$$

$$\begin{array}{r} 426 \\ +122 \\ \hline \end{array}$$
$$\begin{array}{r} 154 \\ +532 \\ \hline \end{array}$$
$$\begin{array}{r} 350 \\ +\ 19 \\ \hline \end{array}$$
$$\begin{array}{r} 625 \\ +170 \\ \hline \end{array}$$

$$\begin{array}{r} 483 \\ +311 \\ \hline \end{array}$$
$$\begin{array}{r} 521 \\ +250 \\ \hline \end{array}$$
$$\begin{array}{r} 608 \\ +\ 70 \\ \hline \end{array}$$
$$\begin{array}{r} 723 \\ +265 \\ \hline \end{array}$$

SPECTRUM MATHEMATICS,
Brown Book–Second Edition

Perfect score: 14    My score: _____

## Addition (3 digit)

Add.

```
  265        894        307        214
 +123        + 5       +141       +625
 ‾‾‾‾‾       ‾‾‾‾‾      ‾‾‾‾‾      ‾‾‾‾‾
  388        899
```

```
  398        420        571        600
 +200       +419       +127       +286
 ‾‾‾‾‾       ‾‾‾‾‾      ‾‾‾‾‾      ‾‾‾‾‾
```

```
  133        512        286        754
 + 30       +487       + 11       +221
 ‾‾‾‾‾       ‾‾‾‾‾      ‾‾‾‾‾      ‾‾‾‾‾
```

```
  530        414        670        265
 +341       +352       + 3        +334
 ‾‾‾‾‾       ‾‾‾‾‾      ‾‾‾‾‾      ‾‾‾‾‾
```

```
  435        342        710        621
 +450       +204       +160       +153
 ‾‾‾‾‾       ‾‾‾‾‾      ‾‾‾‾‾      ‾‾‾‾‾
```

```
  642        531        904        532
 +325       +264       + 25       +302
 ‾‾‾‾‾       ‾‾‾‾‾      ‾‾‾‾‾      ‾‾‾‾‾
```

## Problems

Solve each problem.

There are 236 boys in school.

There are 250 girls in school.

How many boys and girls are in school?

$$\begin{array}{r} 236 \\ +250 \\ \hline \end{array}$$

Mary saw 131 cars.

Marvin saw 268 trucks.

How many cars and trucks did they see in all?

$$+\phantom{000}$$

Jack has 427 pennies.

Jill has 370 pennies.

How many pennies do they have in all?

$$+\phantom{000}$$

There are 582 red apples.

There are 206 yellow apples.

How many apples are there in all?

$$+\phantom{000}$$

Ann found 122 shells.

Pedro found 76 shells.

How many shells did they find?

$$+\phantom{000}$$

SPECTRUM MATHEMATICS,
Brown Book–Second Edition

Perfect score: 5    My score: _____

# Subtracting Hundreds

| 7 hundreds | 700 | | 9 hundreds | 900 |
|---|---|---|---|---|
| −4 hundreds | −400 | | −2 hundreds | −200 |
| 3 hundreds | 300 | | 7 hundreds | 700 |

## Subtract.

| 8 hundreds | 800 | | 2 hundreds | 200 |
|---|---|---|---|---|
| −6 hundreds | −600 | | −1 hundred | −100 |
| hundreds | | | hundred | |

| 500 | 300 | 600 | 400 |
|---|---|---|---|
| −200 | −100 | −500 | −200 |

| 900 | 400 | 800 | 500 |
|---|---|---|---|
| −800 | −300 | −400 | −400 |

| 300 | 600 | 900 | 700 |
|---|---|---|---|
| −200 | −300 | −600 | −100 |

| 700 | 800 | 600 | 900 |
|---|---|---|---|
| −500 | −700 | −400 | −400 |

SPECTRUM MATHEMATICS,
Brown Book—Second Edition

Perfect score: 20   My score: _____

# Subtraction (3 digit)

| Subtract the ones. | | Subtract the tens. | | Subtract the hundreds. |
|---|---|---|---|---|
| 648<br>−523<br>——<br>5 | ⟹ | 648<br>−523<br>——<br>25 | ⟹ | 648<br>−523<br>——<br>125 |

## Subtract.

```
  7 5 9
−   3 0
———————
  7 2 9
```
↳ Subtract the ones.
↳ Subtract the tens.
↳ Subtract the hundreds.

```
  4 6 3
− 1 2 2
```
↳ Subtract the ones.
↳ Subtract the tens.
↳ Subtract the hundreds.

```
  8 6 4      5 2 9      4 7 6      6 5 7
− 3 1 4    − 3 1 7    −   6 2    − 4 2 3
```

```
  6 2 9      8 9 2      9 0 4      7 8 7
− 3 0 9    − 2 3 1    − 6 0 3    − 4 4 4
```

```
  9 9 3      7 4 1      7 5 8      8 6 5
− 5 8 1    − 2 3 0    −   4 6    − 1 6 4
```

SPECTRUM MATHEMATICS,
Brown Book–Second Edition

Perfect score: 14    My score: _____

## Subtract.

| | | | |
|---|---|---|---|
| 956<br>−354<br>**602** | 524<br>− 3<br>**521** | 423<br>−101 | 219<br>− 5 |
| 467<br>−330 | 357<br>−237 | 885<br>− 41 | 768<br>−236 |
| 938<br>−731 | 495<br>−165 | 396<br>− 24 | 452<br>−241 |
| 642<br>−541 | 785<br>−120 | 639<br>− 8 | 879<br>−721 |
| 539<br>−225 | 490<br>−320 | 581<br>−231 | 672<br>−232 |
| 865<br>−563 | 734<br>−412 | 677<br>−156 | 989<br>−344 |

**Problems**

Solve each problem.

There were 237 oranges in a box.

Al took 115 oranges from the box.

How many oranges are still in the box?

$$\begin{array}{r} 237 \\ -\ 115 \\ \hline \end{array}$$

---

There are 486 birds at the zoo.

25 of the birds cannot fly.

How many of the birds can fly?

$-\ \underline{\phantom{xxxxx}}$

---

Mr. Smith had 592 dollars.

He spent 301 dollars.

How many dollars does he have left?

$-\ \underline{\phantom{xxxxx}}$

---

Maria found 175 shells.

Only 34 shells were not broken.

How many shells were broken?

$-\ \underline{\phantom{xxxxx}}$

---

There are 334 children.

There are 212 boys.

How many girls are there?

$-\ \underline{\phantom{xxxxx}}$

SPECTRUM MATHEMATICS,
Brown Book–Second Edition

Perfect score: 5     My score: _____

# Three-Digit Numbers

Write the numeral.

| 1 hundred 0 tens 5 ones | 9 hundreds 6 tens 4 ones |
|---|---|
| _____ | _____ |
| 6 hundreds 1 ten 8 ones | 3 hundreds 2 tens 7 ones |
| _____ | _____ |

Count by tens. Complete the row.

460, 470, ____, ____, ____, ____, 520

Add.

$$
\begin{array}{r} 348 \\ +521 \\ \hline \end{array}
\qquad
\begin{array}{r} 165 \\ +433 \\ \hline \end{array}
\qquad
\begin{array}{r} 497 \\ +100 \\ \hline \end{array}
\qquad
\begin{array}{r} 203 \\ +\ 46 \\ \hline \end{array}
$$

Subtract.

$$
\begin{array}{r} 962 \\ -631 \\ \hline \end{array}
\qquad
\begin{array}{r} 831 \\ -420 \\ \hline \end{array}
\qquad
\begin{array}{r} 974 \\ -564 \\ \hline \end{array}
\qquad
\begin{array}{r} 508 \\ -\ \ 7 \\ \hline \end{array}
$$

$$
\begin{array}{r} 728 \\ -326 \\ \hline \end{array}
\qquad
\begin{array}{r} 657 \\ -\ 45 \\ \hline \end{array}
\qquad
\begin{array}{r} 894 \\ -464 \\ \hline \end{array}
\qquad
\begin{array}{r} 596 \\ -352 \\ \hline \end{array}
$$

SPECTRUM MATHEMATICS,
Brown Book–Second Edition

Perfect score: 22     My score: _____

# Checkup

Write the numeral.

| 2 hundreds 5 tens 6 ones | 8 hundreds 0 tens 4 ones |
|:---:|:---:|
| _____ | _____ |
| 3 hundreds 7 tens 1 one | 7 hundreds 1 ten 9 ones |
| _____ | _____ |

Name the numbers in order.

497, 498, _____, _____, _____, _____

Add.

```
  124        520        739        861
 +323       +407       +150        + 6
```

```
  422        383        146        698
 +314       +105       +532       +101
```

Subtract.

```
  798        694        618        790
 -544       -372       -202       - 60
```

# Answers for
# SPECTRUM MATHEMATICS (Brown Book, Second Edition)

**Page 1**

```
3                 1
5                 0
2                 6
8      10     9        7       4
0    1    2    3    4    5
   6     7     8     9    10
```

**Page 2**

```
 2    1    3    3    2    1
```

| 4 4 | 4 | 4 4 |
|---|---|---|
| 3 1 | 2 | 4 0 |
| 5 5 | 5 5 | 5 5 |
| 3 2 | 4 1 | 5 0 |

**Page 3**

```
 6    6       5          1
```

| 6 3 | 6 6 | 4 2 |
|---|---|---|
| 7 7 | 7 7 | 7 7 |
| 4 3 | 5 2 | 6 1 |

```
 6    7    6        0    3    4
```

**Page 4**

```
 8    8          5          3
```

| 8 | 8 8 | 8 8 |
|---|---|---|
| 4 | 6 2 | 7 1 |
| 8 7 | 6 8 | 8 8 |
| 7 1 | 3 3 | 8 6 |

**Page 5**

```
 9    9          5          4
```

| 9 9 | 9 9 | 9 9 |
|---|---|---|
| 6 3 | 7 2 | 8 1 |
| 9 9 | 7 9 | 9 8 |
| 4 4 | 1 6 | 0 9 |

**Page 6**

| 10 | 10 10 | 10 10 |
|---|---|---|
| 5 | 6 4 | 7 3 |
| 10 10 | | 10 10 |
| 8 2 | | 9 1 |
| 10 10 10 | | 2 7 10 |

**Page 7**

```
5   7   9   10    3    0
2   5   8   10    2    0
5   4   6   8    8    9
9   7   3   8   10    8
6   5   9   10   10    4
9   7   7   10    9    8
```

**Page 8**

```
7   3   3   2   4   0
4   1   2   5   0   0
7   2   2   4   5   1
4   6   2   1   1   5
6   8   5   2   1   0
6   3   1   7   3   3
```

**Page 9**

```
  4        6        4        5        6
 +3       -3       +4       -2       +3
 ──       ──       ──       ──       ──
  7        3        8        3        9
```

**Page 10**

```
6   10    9    8    5    4
7    6   10    6   10    3
4    7    9    7    9   10
0    3    4    7    4    5
8    1    1    2    3    2
3    1    3    2    1    4
```

**Page 11**

```
1 ten 1 one  = 11
1 ten 2 ones = 12
1 ten 3 ones = 13
1 ten 4 ones = 14
1 ten 5 ones = 15
1 ten 6 ones = 16
1 ten 7 ones = 17
1 ten 8 ones = 18
```

**Page 12**

| 2 | 20 | | 2 | 5 | 25 |
|---|---|---|---|---|---|
| 1 | 9 | 19 | 2 | 8 | 28 |
| 3 | | 30 | 3 | 2 | 32 |
| 2 | 6 | 26 | 3 | 8 | 38 |

**Page 13**

| 4 | | 40 | | 4 | 2 | 42 |
|---|---|---|---|---|---|---|
| 5 | 6 | 56 | | 6 | 5 | 65 |
| 7 | | 70 | | 7 | 9 | 79 |
| 8 | 7 | 87 | | 9 | 3 | 93 |

**Page 14**

| 4 | 4 | 44 | | 4 | 3 | 43 |
|---|---|---|---|---|---|---|
| 5 | | 50 | | 5 | 8 | 58 |
| 6 | 6 | 66 | | 7 | 2 | 72 |
| 8 | | 80 | | 9 | 9 | 99 |

**Page 15**

```
46            21
12            57
37   78       19   41
24   11       88   34
90   84       67   66
60   35       72   89
53   49       95   20
     96            50
```

**Page 16**

| 0 | 1 | 2 | 3 | 4 | 5 | 6 | 7 | 8 | 9 |
|---|---|---|---|---|---|---|---|---|---|
| 10 | 11 | 12 | 13 | 14 | 15 | 16 | 17 | 18 | 19 |
| 20 | 21 | 22 | 23 | 24 | 25 | 26 | 27 | 28 | 29 |
| 30 | 31 | 32 | 33 | 34 | 35 | 36 | 37 | 38 | 39 |
| 40 | 41 | 42 | 43 | 44 | 45 | 46 | 47 | 48 | 49 |
| 50 | 51 | 52 | 53 | 54 | 55 | 56 | 57 | 58 | 59 |

**Page 17**

```
 9   10   11   12
25   26   27   28
40   41   42   43
18   19   20   21
54   55   56   57
47   48   49   50
79   80   81   82
85   86   87   88
71   72   73   74
89   90   91   92
58   59   60   61
96   97   98   99
```

**Page 18**

91

## Page 19

```
8 3 9 5    5 3 2    3
E A C H    H A S    A
5 8 3 4    3 1 4
H E A D    A N D
3   0 3 6 7
A   T A I L
```

## Page 20

```
28 | 50
31 | 45
70 | 82
66 | 98
90 | 79

 7   8   9  10
40  41  42  43
56  57  58  59
64  65  66  67
81  82  83  84
89  90  91  92
```

## Page 21

```
2              5
      10
4              7
```

## Page 22

```
 5    1
 7    4
11   10
 8   13
```

## Page 23

```
1    2
4    3
  6
```

## Page 24

```
2          7
    4
2          1
           3
5
4
```

## Page 25

```
4    7
9    5
3    2
  5
```

## Page 26

```
11 | 11 | 3 | 8
11 | 11 | 2 | 9
11 | 11 | 5 | 6
11 | 11 | 4 | 7
11 11 11 | 5  2  4
11 11 11 | 9 11  3
```

## Page 27

```
12 | 12 | 4 | 8
12 | 12 | 3 | 9
12 | 12 | 5 | 7
12 |      6
12 12 12 | 6 12 4
12 12 12 | 7  3 8
```

## Page 28

```
12 11 12 12 11 11
10 12 10 12 12 11
10 11 11 11 12 11
 4  2  7  7  6 11
 9  5  7  3  4  6
12  9  2  8  4  3
```

## Page 29

```
 8   6   7   9   5
+3  +6  +5  +2  +6
11  12  12  11  11
```

## Page 30

```
12  11  12  11  12
-4  -2  -3  -4  -5
 8   9   9   7   7
```

## Page 31

```
13 | 13 | 6 | 7
13 | 13 | 5 | 8
13 | 13 | 4 | 9
13 13 13 | 8 6 4
13 13 13 | 9 5 7
```

## Page 32

```
14 | 14 | 5 | 9
14 | 14 | 6 | 8
14 |      7
14 14 12 | 6 5 9
13 14 11 | 7 5 8
14 13 14 | 3 5 8
```

## Page 33

```
13 14 11 12 14 11
11 14 12 13 13 14
11 12 14 13 13 12
 7  6  9  8  7  7
 5  3  8  6  5  6
 4  2  9  4  4  6
```

## Page 34

```
 8   6   9   8   7
+6  +7  +5  +5  +7
14  13  14  13  14
```

## Page 35

```
13  14  13  14  13
-4  -8  -6  -5  -9
 9   6   7   9   4
```

## Page 36

```
15 | 15 | 8 | 7
15 | 15 | 9 | 6
15 15 14 | 5 7 6
14 14 15 | 6 8 8
13 15 14 | 5 9 9
```

## Page 37

```
16 | 16 | 9 | 7
      16 |    8
15 16 15 | 7 8 9
16 14 14 | 5 9 8
16 14 15 | 6 9 6
```

## Page 38

```
15 12 14 12 14 15
16 13 13 14 16 11
11 15 16 13 14 15
 7  9  9  5  9  3
 6  8  2  8  8  6
 8  4  7  5  7  6
```

## Page 39

```
 8   8   7   9   8
+7  +8  +9  +6  +7
15  16  16  15  15
```

## Page 40

```
16  15  15  16  16
-8  -7  -6  -7  -9
 8   8   9   9   7
```

## Page 41

```
17 | 17 | 9 | 8
      18 |    9
14 16 17 | 9 8 7
16 15 15 | 7 9 8
17 16 18 | 9 8 9
```

## Page 42

```
17 11 13 13 14 14
15 12 10 17 15 11
14 12 10 16 18 16
 9  8  7  9  7  9
 7  4  4  3  9  7
 8  9  9  7  6  8
```

## Page 43

```
 8   9   9   8   9
+9  +8  +9  +9  +9
17  17  18  17  18
```

# Answers for SPECTRUM MATHEMATICS (Brown Book, Second Edition)

## Page 44

| | | | | |
|---|---|---|---|---|
| 17 −8 = 9 | 17 −9 = 8 | 18 −9 = 9 | 17 −8 = 9 | 18 −9 = 9 |

## Page 45

| | | | | | |
|---|---|---|---|---|---|
| 12 | 12 | 11 | 11 | 13 | 13 |
| 10 | 10 | 13 | 13 | 14 | 14 |
| 15 | 15 | 12 | 12 | 15 | 15 |
| 14 | 11 | 11 | 14 | 14 | 16 |
| 10 | 13 | 13 | 17 | 17 | 12 |
| 16 | 16 | 12 | 11 | 10 | 18 |

## Page 46

| | | | |
|---|---|---|---|
| 5 + 6 | 9 + 2 | 6 + 6 | 3 + 9 |
| 4 + 7 | 8 + 3 | 7 + 5 | 8 + 4 |
| 8 + 5 | 7 + 6 | 8 + 6 | 9 + 5 |
| 9 + 4 | 6 + 7 | 6 + 8 | 7 + 7 |
| 8 + 7 | 9 + 6 | | 9 + 7 |
| 6 + 9 | 7 + 8 | 7 + 9 | 8 + 8 |
| 8 + 9 | 9 + 8 | 9 + 9 | |

## Page 47

| | | | | | |
|---|---|---|---|---|---|
| 8 | 7 | 4 | 9 | 4 | 8 |
| 8 | 6 | 4 | 7 | 3 | 7 |
| 9 | 6 | 5 | 9 | 9 | 8 |
| 8 | 9 | 7 | 8 | 5 | 7 |
| 6 | 8 | 3 | 6 | 7 | 5 |
| 2 | 8 | 7 | 5 | 9 | 8 |

## Page 48

3 6 2    5 9 6 8
YOU   KNOW

4 7 4 0 3   6 9 4
EVERY   ONE

3 6 2   8 1 9
YOU   WIN

## Page 49

| | | | | |
|---|---|---|---|---|
| 6 +8 = 14 | 12 −3 = 9 | 8 +7 = 15 | 10 −2 = 8 | 8 +5 = 13 |

## Page 50

| | | | | | |
|---|---|---|---|---|---|
| 17 | 12 | 14 | 12 | 10 | 11 |
| 13 | 16 | 14 | 18 | 15 | 12 |
| 7 | 7 | 0 | 0 | 4 | 7 |
| 5 | 3 | 6 | 9 | 9 | 8 |
| 8 +5 = 13 | | | 11 −5 = 6 | | |

## Page 51

| | |
|---|---|
| 1 2 ½ | 1 2 ½ |
| 1 2 ½ | 1 2 ½ |
| ½ | ½ |

## Page 52

| | |
|---|---|
| 1 3 ⅓ | 1 3 ⅓ |
| 1 3 ⅓ | 1 3 ⅓ |
| ⅓ | ⅓ |

## Page 53

| | |
|---|---|
| 1 4 ¼ | 1 4 ¼ |
| 1 4 ¼ | 1 4 ¼ |
| ¼ | ¼ |

## Page 54

| | | |
|---|---|---|
| ½ ⅓ (¼) | (½) ⅓ ¼ | ½ (⅓) ¼ |
| ½ (⅓) ¼ | ½ ⅓ (¼) | (½) ⅓ ¼ |
| ½ ⅓ (¼) | ½ (⅓) ¼ | (½) ⅓ ¼ |
| ½ (⅓) ¼ | ½ ⅓ (¼) | (½) ⅓ ¼ |

## Page 55

| | | |
|---|---|---|
| 4 o'clock 4:00 | 1 o'clock 1:00 | 12 o'clock 12:00 |
| 9 o'clock 9:00 | 3 o'clock 3:00 | 11 o'clock 11:00 |
| 6 o'clock 6:00 | 10 o'clock 10:00 | 7 o'clock 7:00 |

## Page 56

| | | |
|---|---|---|
| half past 3 3:30 | half past 4 4:30 | half past 5 5:30 |
| half past 10 10:30 | half past 4 4:30 | half past 7 7:30 |
| half past 6 6:30 | half past 12 12:30 | half past 9 9:30 |

## Page 57

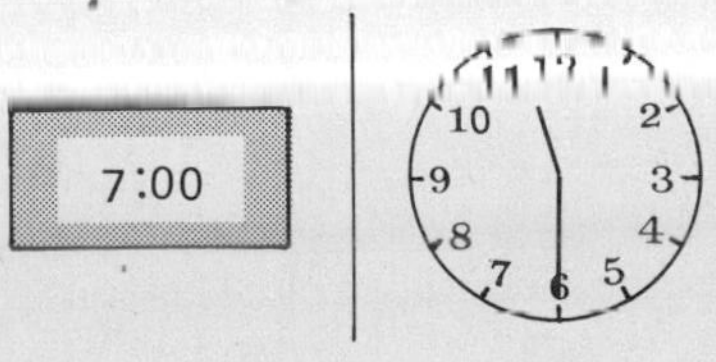

7:00

## Page 57 Continued

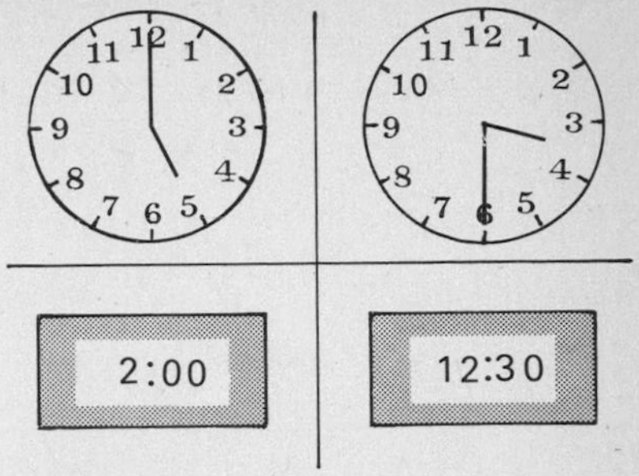

2:00   12:30

## Page 58

| | | |
|---|---|---|
| ½ (⅓) ¼ | (½) ⅓ ¼ | ½ ⅓ (¼) |
| ½ ⅓ (¼) | ½ (⅓) ¼ | ½ ⅓ (¼) |
| half past 7 | 11 o'clock | 3:00 |
| 10:00 | 5:30 | 1:30 |

## Page 59

| | | | | | |
|---|---|---|---|---|---|
| 4 | 9 | 8 | 8 | 6 | 7 |
| 10 | 11 | 12 | 12 | 17 | 13 |
| 13 | 18 | 10 | 15 | 13 | 16 |
| 1 | 2 | 0 | 1 | 3 | 6 |
| 2 | 7 | 6 | 6 | 7 | 7 |
| 7 | 8 | 8 | 2 | 7 | 8 |

## Page 60

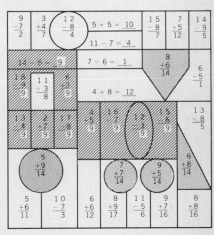

## Page 61

| 4 tens | 40 | | 9 tens | 90 |
|---|---|---|---|---|
| 20 | 70 | 30 | 80 | 90 |
| 50 | 50 | 80 | 60 | 60 |
| 50 | 40 | 90 | 70 | 90 |
| 60 | 80 | 80 | 60 | 80 |

## Page 62

| | | | | |
|---|---|---|---|---|
| 59 | | 70 | 86 | 78 |
| 47 | 89 | 58 | 58 | 64 |
| 25 | 64 | 29 | 97 | 98 |
| 70 | 78 | 96 | 89 | 59 |
| 86 | 96 | 69 | 94 | 98 |

## Page 63

| | | | | |
|---|---|---|---|---|
| 59 | 57 | 40 | 24 | 85 |
| 69 | 16 | 37 | 83 | 89 |
| 76 | 89 | 85 | 94 | 78 |
| 52 | 69 | 63 | 49 | 89 |
| 78 | 48 | 78 | 95 | 69 |
| 94 | 79 | 72 | 89 | 98 |

## Page 64

Rod
Pam

| | |
|---|---|
| 25¢ +20¢ = 45¢ | 20¢ +32¢ = 52¢ |
| 26¢ +20¢ = 46¢ | 32¢ +26¢ = 58¢ |
| 25¢ +32¢ = 57¢ | 20¢ +25¢ = 45¢ |

## Page 65

| 2 tens | 20 | | 2 tens | 20 |
|---|---|---|---|---|
| 10 | 20 | 40 | 30 | 50 |
| 10 | 20 | 10 | 10 | 30 |
| 60 | 10 | 40 | 20 | 30 |
| 50 | 50 | 10 | 40 | 20 |

## Page 66

| | | | | |
|---|---|---|---|---|
| 73 | | 30 | 41 | 30 |
| 64 | 16 | 93 | 41 | 14 |
| 47 | 25 | 43 | 60 | 13 |
| 12 | 10 | 27 | 42 | 57 |
| 18 | 32 | 82 | 43 | 62 |

## Page 67

| | | | | |
|---|---|---|---|---|
| 31 | 82 | 54 | 21 | 72 |
| 33 | 14 | 58 | 15 | 65 |
| 48 | 74 | 74 | 41 | 20 |
| 12 | 46 | 30 | 12 | 27 |
| 10 | 23 | 36 | 12 | 53 |
| 11 | 96 | 41 | 42 | 35 |

## Page 68

| | |
|---|---|
| 45¢ −35¢ = 10¢ | 24¢ −12¢ = 12¢ |
| 45¢ −24¢ = 21¢ | 35¢ −24¢ = 11¢ |
| 35¢ −12¢ = 23¢ | 45¢ −12¢ = 33¢ |

## Page 69

| 8 | 8 | 8 | 9 | 9 | 9 |
|---|---|---|---|---|---|
| 50 | 60 | 60 | 50 | 80 | |
| 58 | 35 | 99 | 67 | 67 | |
| 77 | 94 | 87 | 89 | 85 | |

## Page 70

| 35 | 86 | | 88 | 7 | 68 |
|---|---|---|---|---|---|
| I | T | | W | A | S |
| 86 | 58 | 58 | 9 | 7 | 59 |
| T | O | O | F | A | R |
| 86 | 58 | 88 | 7 | 47 | 39 |
| T | O | W | A | L | K |

## Page 71

| | |
|---|---|
| 50¢ +25¢ = 75¢ | 50¢ +30¢ = 80¢ |
| 25¢ +20¢ = 45¢ | 50¢ +40¢ = 90¢ |
| 50¢ 25¢ +10¢ = 85¢ | 50¢ 25¢ +20¢ = 95¢ |

## Page 72

| | |
|---|---|
| 30¢ +34¢ = 64¢ | 50¢ −30¢ = 20¢ |
| 34¢ +25¢ = 59¢ | 89¢ −25¢ = 64¢ |
| 30¢ +25¢ = 55¢ | 97¢ −34¢ = 63¢ |

## Page 73

| | | | | | |
|---|---|---|---|---|---|
| 57 | 89 | 18 | 45 | 79 | 97 |
| 48 | 66 | 38 | 94 | 76 | 65 |
| 39 | 96 | 39 | 59 | 79 | 89 |
| 76 | 23 | 86 | 42 | 57 | 13 |
| 24 | 50 | 64 | 93 | 10 | 87 |

## Page 74

| | | | | | |
|---|---|---|---|---|---|
| 47 | 66 | 99 | 99 | 94 | 88 |
| 9 | 39 | 89 | 98 | 89 | 67 |
| 22 | 71 | 33 | 70 | 31 | 48 |
| 35 | 41 | 22 | 35 | 40 | 61 |

| | |
|---|---|
| 31¢ −21¢ = 10¢ | 48¢ −23¢ = 25¢ |

## Page 75

| 1 2 3 | 1 6 8 |
|---|---|
| 123 | 168 |
| 1 4 5 | 1 1 7 |
| 145 | 117 |
| 150 | 172 |
| 104 | 199 |

## Page 76

| 2 7 9 | 4 3 0 |
|---|---|
| 279 | 430 |

## Page 76 *Continued*

| 3 5 6 | 3 0 0 |
|---|---|
| 356 | 300 |
| 236 | 340 |
| 499 | 289 |
| 404 | 321 |

266, 267, 268, 269, 270, 271
399, 400, 401, 402, 403, 404

## Page 77

| 5 2 0 | 6 0 0 |
|---|---|
| 520 | 600 |
| 621 | 714 |
| 553 | 697 |
| 678 | 732 |
| 765 | 583 |
| 610 | 776 |
| 799 | 588 |

## Page 78

| 8 2 5 | 9 1 6 |
|---|---|
| 825 | 916 |
| 928 | 842 |
| 892 | 903 |
| 975 | 840 |

200, 300, 400, 500, 600, 700, 800
870, 880, 890, 900, 910, 920, 930

## Page 79

| 864 | 538 |
|---|---|
| 315 | 983 |
| 101 | 427 |

FUN

## Page 80

| | | |
|---|---|---|
| 420 | 819 | 770 |
| 302 | 325 | 345 |
| 144 | 607 | 159 |
| 855 | 256 | 199 |
| 210 | 173 | 422 |
| 689 | 761 | 949 |
| 580 | 940 | 666 |
| 994 | 500 | 180 |
| 630 | 848 | 799 |
| 800 | 584 | 594 |

## Page 81

| 3 hundreds | 300 | 8 hundreds | 800 |
|---|---|---|---|
| 200 | 900 | 800 | 900 |
| 500 | 900 | 400 | 800 |
| 700 | 700 | 500 | 600 |
| 600 | 600 | 400 | 900 |

# Answers for SPECTRUM MATHEMATICS (Brown Book, Second Edition)

**Page 82**

| | | | |
|---|---|---|---|
| 875 | | 819 | |
| 599 | 794 | 857 | 387 |
| 548 | 686 | 369 | 795 |
| 794 | 771 | 678 | 988 |

**Page 83**

| | | | |
|---|---|---|---|
| 388 | 899 | 448 | 839 |
| 598 | 839 | 698 | 886 |
| 163 | 999 | 297 | 975 |
| 871 | 766 | 673 | 599 |
| 885 | 546 | 870 | 774 |
| 967 | 795 | 929 | 894 |

**Page 84**

| | | | | |
|---|---|---|---|---|
| 236 | 131 | 427 | 582 | 122 |
| +250 | +268 | +370 | +206 | +76 |
| 486 | 399 | 797 | 788 | 198 |

**Page 85**

| | | | |
|---|---|---|---|
| 2 hundreds 200 | | 1 hundred 100 | |
| 300 | 200 | 100 | 200 |
| 100 | 100 | 400 | 100 |

**Page 85** *Continued*

| | | | |
|---|---|---|---|
| 100 | 300 | 300 | 600 |
| 200 | 100 | 200 | 500 |

**Page 86**

| | | | |
|---|---|---|---|
| 729 | | 341 | |
| 550 | 212 | 414 | 234 |
| 320 | 661 | 301 | 343 |
| 412 | 511 | 712 | 701 |

**Page 87**

| | | | |
|---|---|---|---|
| 602 | 521 | 322 | 214 |
| 137 | 120 | 844 | 532 |
| 207 | 330 | 372 | 211 |
| 101 | 665 | 631 | 158 |
| 314 | 170 | 350 | 440 |
| 302 | 322 | 521 | 645 |

**Page 88**

| | | | | |
|---|---|---|---|---|
| 237 | 486 | 592 | 175 | 334 |
| −115 | −25 | −301 | −34 | −212 |
| 122 | 461 | 291 | 141 | 122 |

**Page 89**

| | | |
|---|---|---|
| 105 | | 964 |
| | 618 | 327 |

470, 480, 490, 500, 510, 520

| | | | |
|---|---|---|---|
| 869 | 598 | 597 | 249 |
| 331 | 411 | 410 | 501 |
| 402 | 612 | 430 | 244 |

**Page 90**

| | | |
|---|---|---|
| 256 | | 804 |
| | 371 | 719 |

499, 500, 501, 502

| | | | |
|---|---|---|---|
| 447 | 927 | 889 | 867 |
| 736 | 488 | 678 | 799 |
| 254 | 322 | 416 | 730 |